MIRRORS AND IMAGES

Senior Authors
Carl B. Smith
Virginia A. Arnold

Linguistics Consultant
Ronald Wardhaugh

Macmillan Publishing Company
New York

Collier Macmillan Publishers
London

This work is also published in individual volumes under
the titles: *Stand Tall* and *A Second Look,* copyright ©
1983 Macmillan Publishing Co., Inc. Parts of this work
were published in earlier editions of SERIES r.

Macmillan Publishing Company
866 Third Avenue, New York, New York 10022
Collier Macmillan Canada, Inc.

Printed in the United States of America
ISBN 0-02-136700-0
9 8 7 6 5 4 3 2

ACKNOWLEDGMENTS

The publisher gratefully acknowledges permission to reprint the following copyrighted material:

"Always the Same," (original title "Some things I want to have different and new. . . ."), from *I Wonder Why* by Ruth P. Harnden. Copyright © 1971 by Ruth P. Harnden. Used by permission of Houghton Mifflin Company and Russell and Volkening, Inc.

"Dick Thompson—The Selfish Boy," adapted text excerpt of "The Selfishness Cure," from *Mrs. Piggle-Wiggle* by Betty MacDonald. Text copyright © 1947 by Betty MacDonald. Renewed 1975 by Donald C. MacDonald. By permission of J. B. Lippincott, Publishers, and A. M. Heath & Company Ltd. for the Estate of Betty MacDonald.

"The Fastest Quitter in Town," adapted from *The Fastest Quitter in Town* by Phyllis Green. Text © copyright 1972 by Phyllis Green. A Young Scott Book, by permission of Addison-Wesley Publishing Company, Inc.

"Gordon the Goat," adapted from *Gordon the Goat* by Munro Leaf. Copyright © 1944, 1972 by Munro Leaf. Reprinted by permission of Margaret Leaf.

"I Don't Know Why," from *Whispers and Other Poems* by Myra Cohn Livingston. Copyright © 1958 by Myra Cohn Livingston. Reprinted by permission of Harcourt Brace Jovanovich, Publishers.

"Impossible, Possum," from *Impossible, Possum* by Ellen Conford. Copyright © 1971 by Ellen Conford. By permission of Little, Brown and Co.

"The Knee-High Man," excerpted from *The Knee-High Man and Other Tales* by Julius Lester. Copyright © 1972 by Julius Lester. Reprinted by permission of The Dial Press.

"Poetry of the Papago Indian Tribe": "Come All!" and "At the edge of the world," from *Singing for Power* by Ruth Murray Underhill. Copyright © 1938 by The Regents of the University of California. Reprinted by permission of the University of California Press.

"Rain Pools," from *I Thought I Heard the City* by Lilian Moore. Copyright © 1969 by Lilian Moore. Used by permission of Atheneum Publishers.

"Six Foolish Fishermen," from *Six Foolish Fishermen* by Benjamin Elkin. Copyright © 1957 by Childrens Press. Adaptation reprinted by permission of Childrens Press.

"Soup for the King," adapted from *Soup for the King* by Leonard Kessler. Copyright © 1969 by Grosset & Dunlap, Inc. Published by Grosset & Dunlap, Inc.

"Sticks, Stones," adapted from *Sticks, Stones* by Carlos Antonio Llerena Aguirre. Copyright © 1977 by Carlos Antonio Llerena. Reprinted by permission of Holt, Rinehart and Winston, Publishers.

"Tall Tina," from *Tall Tina* by Muriel Stanek. Copyright © 1971 by Muriel Stanek. Reprinted by permission of Albert Whitman & Company.

"What's Fun Without a Friend?" from *What's Fun Without a Friend?* by Chihiro Iwasaki. Copyright © 1972 by Shiko-Sha. Used with permission of McGraw-Hill Book Company and Adam and Charles Black Publishers.

"What Someone Said When He Was Spanked on the Day Before His Birthday," from *You Know Who* by John Ciardi. Copyright © 1964 by John Ciardi. Reprinted by permission of J. B. Lippincott, Publishers.

"Who Am I?" reprinted from *At the Top of My Voice and Other Poems* by Felice Holman. Copyright © 1970 by Felice Holman. Published by Grosset & Dunlap, Inc.

Illustrations: Angela Adams, Don Almquist, Richard Brown, Ray Cruz, Len Ebert, Jack Endewelt, James Foote, George Gaadt, Don Gates, Doug Gervasi, Cheryl Griesbach, Roberto Innocenti, Robert Jackson, Kiki Janovitz, Dora Leder, Stanislaus Martucci, Diane Patterson, Larry Ross, Luciana Rosselli, Donald Silverstein, Fran Stiles, Carol Taback, Charles Varner, Lauren West, Jennie Williams. **Photographs:** James Foote, Victoria Beller Smith.

Contents

7

STAND TALL

People can share things with each other
all the time. Sometimes they share things
they know. Other times they share things
they can do. Everyone has something special
to share with other people. You should be
proud of the things you have to share.

In "Stand Tall," you will read about a girl
who finds out what she can share. You
will read about someone who learns to think
for himself. You will read about a man who
is proud to be who he is. As you read,
think about what people share with each
other. What can you share with someone?

Robert Louis Stevenson

(1850 - 1894)

Robert Louis Stevenson was born in Scotland. He was sick for most of his life. When he was a child, he had to stay in bed much of the time. But he was busy reading books.

When he was older, he went to see other countries. He liked being a traveler. He wanted to write about the places he had seen.

Stevenson wrote many books. One of his books is *A Child's Garden of Verses*. He wrote this book of poems for children. But the poems of Robert Louis Stevenson are loved by people of all ages.

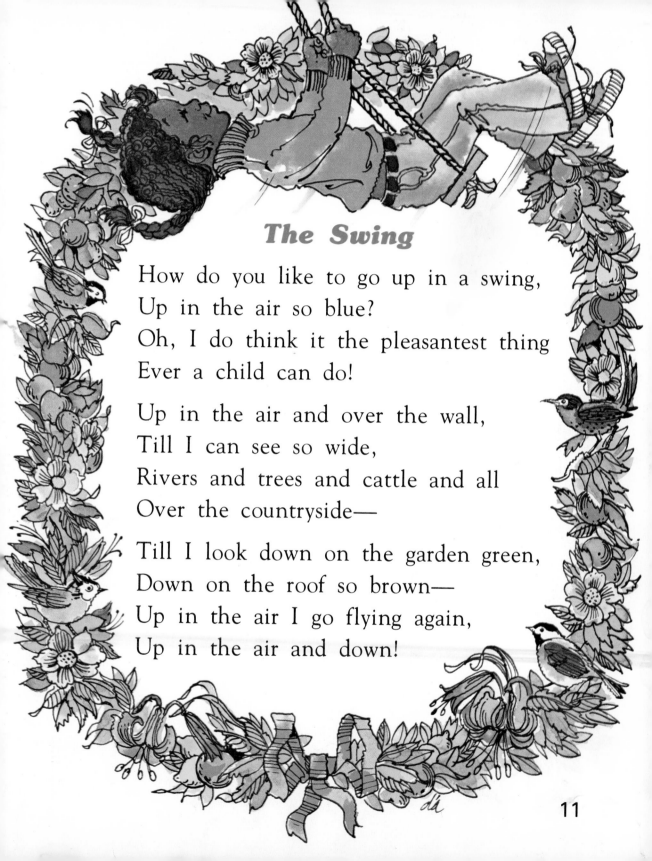

The Swing

How do you like to go up in a swing,
Up in the air so blue?
Oh, I do think it the pleasantest thing
Ever a child can do!

Up in the air and over the wall,
Till I can see so wide,
Rivers and trees and cattle and all
Over the countryside—

Till I look down on the garden green,
Down on the roof so brown—
Up in the air I go flying again,
Up in the air and down!

Bed in Summer

In winter I get up at night
And dress by yellow candle-light.
In summer, quite the other way.
I have to go to bed by day.

I have to go to bed and see
The birds still hopping on the tree,
Or hear the grown-up people's feet
Still going past me in the street.

And does it not seem hard to you,
When all the sky is clear and blue,
And I should like so much to play,
To have to go to bed by day?

Impossible, Possum

Ellen Conford

Part One
A Special Problem

Randolph was a young possum. He had a special problem.

"I don't understand it," his mother said. "All possums hang by their tails and sleep upside down. Why can't you?"

"I don't know," Randolph said sadly. "I really do try hard."

"Try again," said his father. "Maybe you just need to try a little more."

"All right," sighed Randolph. He moved very slowly out onto a branch of their tree. He wound his tail around the branch, took a big breath, and let go. He didn't fall.

"He's doing it!" yelled his brother
Eugene.

"No, he's not," said his sister
Geraldine. Randolph's tail opened, and
he fell to the ground, head first.

"Dear me!" said his mother.
"Are you hurt?"

"No more than all the other times I
fell," said Randolph. "I think I'm all right."

15

"I just don't understand," his father said. "All possums know how to hang upside down."

"It's impossible—just impossible," Randolph sighed. "You might as well get used to it—I'm a flop. I can't hang by my tail."

"No, you're not a flop," said his mother kindly. "You just have to keep trying."

"But every time I try," cried Randolph, "I fall on my head. That hurts!"

"We could put a big pile of leaves under the tree," Eugene said. "Then if you fall, you will fall on something soft."

16

"*If* he falls! You mean, *when* he falls," laughed Geraldine.

"Now, now, Geraldine," said her father. "It's a very good idea. Go help your brothers find some leaves."

Randolph, Eugene, and Geraldine ran around looking for leaves. After a while, they had made a big pile of them under the branch.

"Here I go again," sighed Randolph. He climbed slowly up the tree and out onto the branch. He wound his tail around it, and let go. His tail opened, and he fell head first into the pile of leaves.

Again and again he tried to hang by his tail. Again and again he fell onto the pile of leaves, head first. His brother and sister went off to play. His mother and father went for a walk.

Randolph went on hanging and falling, hanging and falling. At last he gave up.

"No more," he said to himself, as he lay on his back in the leaves. "Maybe other possums can sleep upside down, but I can't. When my family goes to sleep hanging upside down on the branch, I will sleep on my pile of leaves. It's really very soft down here. Come to think of it, it's so nice I think I'll go to sleep right now." And he did.

Part Two
Sap Helps

Randolph woke up to find that Geraldine and Eugene were jumping into his pile of leaves. "This is fun!" yelled Geraldine.

"It may be fun for you," Randolph sighed. "For me it's just a place to sleep." He got up and cleaned himself off. A few leaves stuck to his tail.

"I'll help you," said Eugene. He pulled hard and came away with a leaf in his paw.

"Don't!" said Randolph. "That hurts."

"Look!" Geraldine said. Something was slowly falling from the end of the branch.

"Sap!" she said. "You got sap on your tail, and that's why the leaves stuck to it."

Randolph stopped picking
leaves from his tail. "Why didn't
I think of this before?" he cried.
"If sap makes leaves stick to my
tail, maybe it will make my tail
stick to the branch."

Randolph held his tail under the sap.
Then he ran up the tree, and wound
his tail around a branch. He held on
with his paws until he was sure
the sap was sticking.

Then he opened
his paws and hung down.

He didn't fall!

"Look at me!" he yelled. "Look, everyone!" His mother and father came running.

"Good for you, Randolph!" said his father. "You see, you just had to keep trying."

"I don't think it was that," said Randolph. "I think it was the sap."

"But how is he going to get down?" asked Geraldine.

"I never thought of that," Randolph said.

"It's all right," his mother said kindly. "We will just unwind your tail for you when you want to come down."

"Well, don't unwind it now. I think I'll just hang here for a while," said Randolph. "I might even take a little nap."

From then on, Randolph held his tail under the sap before the possums went to sleep. His mother had to unwind it for him when he woke up.

But one day, Randolph could not find any sap on the tree.

"What will I do now?" he cried.

"Randolph," said his father, "winter is coming. In the winter, sap dries up. You must try to hang like the rest of us, without sap."

"It's impossible," said Randolph to himself. "I just can't do it without sap."

Just then, Geraldine ran over to him. "Look," she said, "I found more sap, and I put it on this leaf. Would you like me to rub it on your tail?"

"That's very nice of you, Geraldine," said Randolph, and he held out his tail.

Then he ran up the tree. "Geraldine found some more sap," called Randolph. He had opened his paws and was hanging by his tail. "It works! Thank you, Geraldine."

Everyone came over to look. Then Geraldine yelled, "Randolph, you're doing it! Look at Randolph! He's doing it!"

"Sure he's doing it," said Eugene. "He can always do it with the sap on his tail."

"No, no, no!" cried Geraldine, jumping up and down. "It wasn't sap, it was water! I put water on the leaf. It was a trick!"

"Water?" cried Randolph.

"That was a mean trick, Geraldine," said Eugene.

"But he is hanging by his tail!" Geraldine said. "By himself! With no sap!"

"Randolph, this is wonderful! I'm so proud of you!" said his mother.

"I can do it! I can do it!" Randolph yelled.

"You just had to think you could do it," said his father.

"You just needed a tricky sister," said Eugene.

"You mean a smart sister," said Geraldine.

The possums were so happy that they ran out onto the branch and sang "He's a Jolly Good Possum" to Randolph, who was hanging upside down by his tail.

And no one sang louder than Randolph.

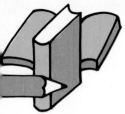

What Comes Next?

A. Read the story. Then read each question. Choose the correct answer. Write it on your paper.

Carmen wanted to go fishing with Uncle Rico. She went into the garage. Carmen took her fishing pole off the wall. Then she got her father's fishing box. At last Carmen was ready to meet Uncle Rico.

1. What did Carmen do first?
   Carmen took her fishing pole off the wall.
   Carmen went into the garage.
   Carmen went fishing with Uncle Rico.

   1. Carmen went into the garage.

2. What did Carmen do last?
   Carmen went to meet her Uncle Rico.
   Carmen went into the garage.
   Carmen wanted to go fishing.

Something to Share

Francisco Jimenez

Part One
Anita's Problem

Anita sat quietly. She listened to John as he shared his rock collection with the class. When he was done, all the boys and girls clapped.

"That was very nice, John," said Mrs. Green. "Now, let me see. Who's going to share next time? Ben shared his paper dragons. Betsy shared her pretty dolls from Japan, and Andy shared his collection of toy cars." Mrs. Green looked around the class. "Oh, yes, Monday will be Anita's turn to share something with us."

When Anita heard this, she wanted to hide. She knew her turn was coming, but not this soon. Later, when the class went to the playground, Anita did not want to play. She sat on the grass.

"What's the matter, Anita?" asked her friend Kim. "You're so quiet. Do you feel sick?"

"No, I'm fine," said Anita. "I just don't know what I'm going to share with the class on Monday. I've been thinking about it for a long time."

"Today is only Friday," said Kim. "You have two more days to think of something."

"I know," said Anita. "But that isn't very long."

When Anita got home that afternoon, her grandma and her little brother Paco were in the living room.

"How was school, Anita?" asked Grandma.

"Fine, Grandma," said Anita.

Paco ran up and gave Anita a hug. "Will you play with me?" he asked.

Anita smiled. "Not now, Paco. I have to help Grandma clean the living room and make dinner before Mama and Papa come home from the store."

"Are you going to help Mama and Papa at the store tomorrow?" asked Grandma.

"Oh, yes," said Anita.

The living room was clean and dinner was ready when Mama and Papa came home. The whole family sat at the table to eat.

Anita was quiet for a while. Then she looked at Papa and said, "Papa, can I stay home Monday? I can help you at the store."

"You can help us at the store tomorrow," said Papa. "On Monday you have to go to school."

"Papa is right," said Mama. "But why don't you want to go to school on Monday?"

Anita looked down. She thought of how the class had clapped for John. She didn't know what to say.

"You don't have to tell us if you don't want to, but maybe we can help you," said Papa.

Anita wanted to tell them, but she decided to wait. She wanted to think of something to share on her own.

When Anita went to bed that night, she couldn't sleep for a while. "I will have to think of something tomorrow," she thought as she fell asleep at last.

Part Two
Anita's Idea

The next day after breakfast,
Papa, Mama, and Anita drove down
Los Angeles Street to the store.

Anita saw the big sign in the window:

All morning Anita helped her Mama
and Papa clean the shop. But work did
not stop her from thinking, "What will I
share on Monday?"

Late in the morning, Anita saw
John and his mother coming into
the store.

"Anita!" said John. "I didn't know you worked here."

"This is our store," said Anita.

"Wow!" said John. "Look at all the great toys and things you have here. Where did you get these?"

"All these things are made in Mexico," said Anita's papa. "They are sent here to Los Angeles by truck."

John picked up something that looked like a ball. "What is this?" he asked.

"That is a balero," said Anita. "Haven't you ever seen one before?"

"No, never," said John. "This is the first time I've seen any of these things."

"Really?" said Anita. She thought for a while. Then she almost yelled, "I have something to share!"

"You mean with our class?" said John.

"Yes," said Anita. "I'm going to take this balero and some of these things to share in class."

"That's a great idea," said John. "Will you show us how to play with the balero?"

"Sure," said Anita. "I'll show everyone on Monday."

Monday morning Anita looked very pretty when she walked into the classroom. Her jet black eyes were very bright.

When sharing time came, Mrs. Green looked over at Anita. "It's Anita's turn to share today," she said.

Anita got up and looked at the door. She smiled and said out loud, "You may come in now, Papa." Papa walked in with a box of Mexican things from the store.

"This is my papa," said Anita. "His name is Mr. Perez. He's going to show you many nice things from Mexico." All the boys and girls clapped.

"Hello, everyone," said Papa. "I'm happy to be here."

"Show us how to play with the balero," John called out.

Anita's papa picked up the balero from the box.

"This is a balero," he said. "Many children play with baleros in Mexico. The balero has two parts. It has a top with a hole in it and a stick. The top hangs from the stick on a string. You have to flip the top and catch it with the stick. The stick goes into the hole in the top part when you catch it."

Mr. Perez showed the class how to
flip the balero. Some of the boys and
girls took turns, too. Then Anita took a
piggy bank from the box.

"This piggy bank is made of clay,"
said Anita. "It is painted red, green,
white, and brown. Boys and girls in
Mexico keep their money in piggy banks
like this one."

Then Mr. Perez took something small
out of the box.

"This is a candy lion," he said.
"We make other animals like donkeys,
coyotes, and horses out of candy, too.
They are very good."

Mr. Perez and Anita showed many
more things from the store. Then
Mr. Perez said, "Now, I'm going to give
each one of you some Mexican candy."
The whole class clapped.

Anita was very happy. She shared
not only many nice things from Mexico,
but she also shared her papa. She was
very proud.

My Farm

Children who live in Mexico or Puerto Rico speak Spanish. Here is a song with some Spanish words.

El perrito means *the dog. Bienvenidos, bienvenidos, venid, venid, venid* means *welcome, welcome, come, come, come.* Sing the song using the other animal names, too.

What's Fun Without a Friend?

Chihiro Iwasaki

Allison stood on the sidewalk in front of her house. She held her little brown dog Tippy in her arms. She was looking at the house across the street.

"Tippy, I have to take you over to Mrs. Johnson," Allison said. "Tomorrow, Mother and I are going to see Grandma at the seashore. It's a vacation. Mother says you can't come with us. You must stay with Mrs. Johnson. Please be good, Tippy."

Allison gave the little dog another big hug.

"Mother says I'll have fun at the seashore. There are children my age. There is a lot of sand and water to play in. There are waves that splash on the beach, too. But I don't think it will be fun without you, Tippy."

The next morning, Allison and her mother drove up to Grandma's house. But Allison was still thinking of Tippy.

"See how pretty the ocean is, Allison. Look how it sparkles in the sunlight," her mother said. "Hurry now, dear. Give Grandma a big hug. There's time for a swim before lunch."

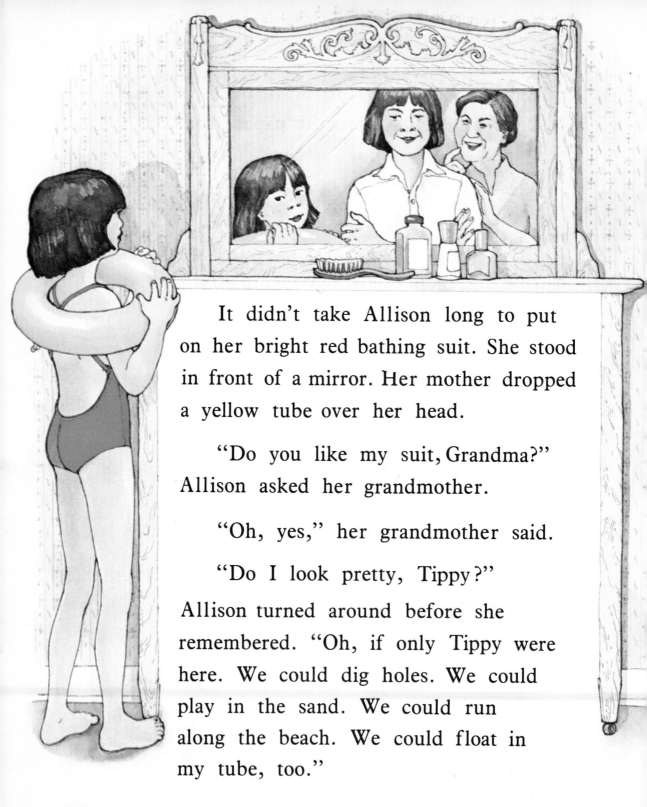

It didn't take Allison long to put on her bright red bathing suit. She stood in front of a mirror. Her mother dropped a yellow tube over her head.

"Do you like my suit, Grandma?" Allison asked her grandmother.

"Oh, yes," her grandmother said.

"Do I look pretty, Tippy?" Allison turned around before she remembered. "Oh, if only Tippy were here. We could dig holes. We could play in the sand. We could run along the beach. We could float in my tube, too."

That night before she went to bed, Allison got a piece of paper from her grandmother. She asked her mother to help her write a letter. Then she wrote:

Dear Tippy,

How are you? You should see my red bathing suit. Grandma says it is very pretty. The ocean is big and cool. Grandma cooks all the things I like to eat. But I miss you. Please ask our daddy to bring you here. You will love Grandma. Her eyes sparkle all the time. You will like the beach, too. I promise I will not swim till you come. So please come soon. I miss you.

Your friend,
Allison

The next morning, Allison put on her big, wide sunhat and stood in the water. A boy playing in the waves yelled, "Hey, where's your bathing suit? Can't you swim?"

But Allison turned and walked away.

When she got back to her grandmother's house, Allison said, "Mother, I want to go home. I know Mrs. Johnson tied Tippy so he can't run away. He always barks and cries when he's tied up. Maybe Mrs. Johnson and some other people will get mad. Let's go home, please, Mother. I'll get my clothes."

Just then, Allison heard a bark. "Oh!" she cried and started to run. "I heard something. . . . Could it be. . . ?"

She got to the door and called, "Oh, Mother! Grandma! Look . . . look who's here! It's Tippy . . . and Daddy! Daddy brought Tippy!"

Allison ran quickly out the door. She picked up the little dog in her arms.

"Thank you, Daddy," she said. "Thank you for bringing Tippy." She tried to hold Tippy and kiss her father at the same time. "Oh, Tippy, we are going to have fun now. Did you get my letter? We'll dig in the sand and run. Come on, Tippy, I want to put on my suit. I'll show that boy I can swim!"

"See, that's the ocean, Tippy," Allison said a few minutes later. She ran across the sand to the water. She wanted to try out her yellow tube.

At first, Tippy just sat in Allison's big sunhat. Then he ran to the water, too. As soon as he jumped into the ocean, Tippy paddled the waves with his little paws. He showed Allison how well he could swim.

After Tippy came to the beach,
Allison did have fun. Each day she and
Tippy played outdoors. They built sand
castles and played games.

By the end of her summer vacation,
Allison could dog-paddle almost as well
as Tippy could.

Tall Tina
Muriel Stanek

Part One
Tiny Tina

When Tina was little, everyone at home called her Tiny Tina. But as she grew taller and taller and went to school, it was just Grandma who still called her Tiny Tina.

"Tiny, please find my green pocketbook," Grandma would say.

"Here it is, Grandma," Tina would call. "Right up here on the shelf."

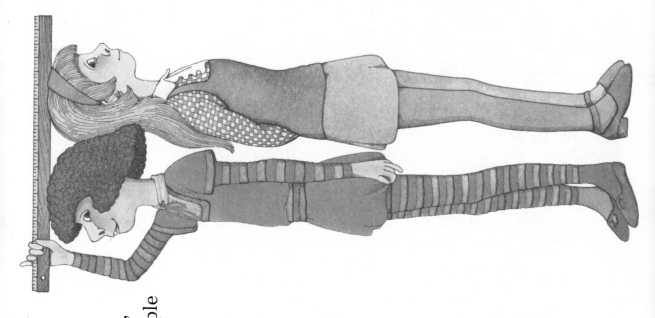

That would make Grandma smile. She would say, "My Tiny Tina is getting tall, and that's fine. There are lots of tall people in our family."

That was so. Most of Tina's family were tall. And Tina liked that. She was proud to look like one of the family.

When Tina's father put Tina and her big sister Maria back to back one day, he said, "Well, what do you know! Tina, you are as tall as Maria."

Tina liked being tall when she and her mother went shopping for new things for Tina. "Let's look at the coats for school-girls," Mother said. "Coats for little girls are too small for you now."

At school, no other girl in her class was as tall as Tina. Most of the time, this was fine with Tina. Miss Smith would say, "Tina, please get the paper from the top shelf."

"Not everyone can do that," Tina would say to herself, as she took the paper from the shelf.

When the class had a spring play, Miss Smith picked Tina to be a tree. Tina thought it might be fun to be one of the little birds. But on the day of the play, Tina was happy that she was a tree. She had on a tall hat made of leaves, and she put her hands way out to make them look like branches. There were other trees, but no tree in the play was as tall as Tina. The music played, and Tina shook her branches over everyone. It was fun.

But sometimes Tina did wish she were not so tall. She didn't like to sit in the last seat in her row.

One morning Tina tried to move up three places. Miss Smith saw her and said, "Tina, you are too tall for that seat. Ben can't see over your head."

Tina walked slowly back to her old seat at the back of the room.

At home, because Tina was so tall, everyone wanted her to act more like Maria. "You are too big to be so silly," her father said when she laughed too much.

"You are too big to cry," her mother said when Tina cut her hand.

Just Grandma still thought of Tina as a little girl. "Tiny Tina," Grandma would say, "come and sit on my lap."

Tina would be happy to have someone to hold her. But when Grandma tried to rock her, Tina's long legs hit the floor. So, after a while, Tina would get down on the floor and sit with her head on Grandma's lap.

Part Two
String Bean Tina

One day a new boy called Rico moved in on Tina's street. He was in her class at school. He was a short boy, but he still looked older than the other children.

In school, when Rico saw Tina looking his way, he made a face at her. When the other children walked out of the room, Rico put his foot out and made Jay fall. Two days after that, on the way home from school, Rico yelled, "Tina is a string bean—String Bean Tina!" Some of the children laughed. Then someone called, "Tall Tina! Look at Tall Tina!"

Tina ran home without looking back at any of the children who were making fun of her.

Next morning there was a paper on Tina's seat. It said, "Tina is a _____" and there was a drawing of a giant.

Tears came into Tina's eyes. "I can't help it if I'm tall," she said to herself. She tried to hide her long legs under her seat.

Going home from school, Tina stopped to look at herself in a bakery window. Then she saw Rico. He was calling, "Tall Tina! String Bean Tina!"

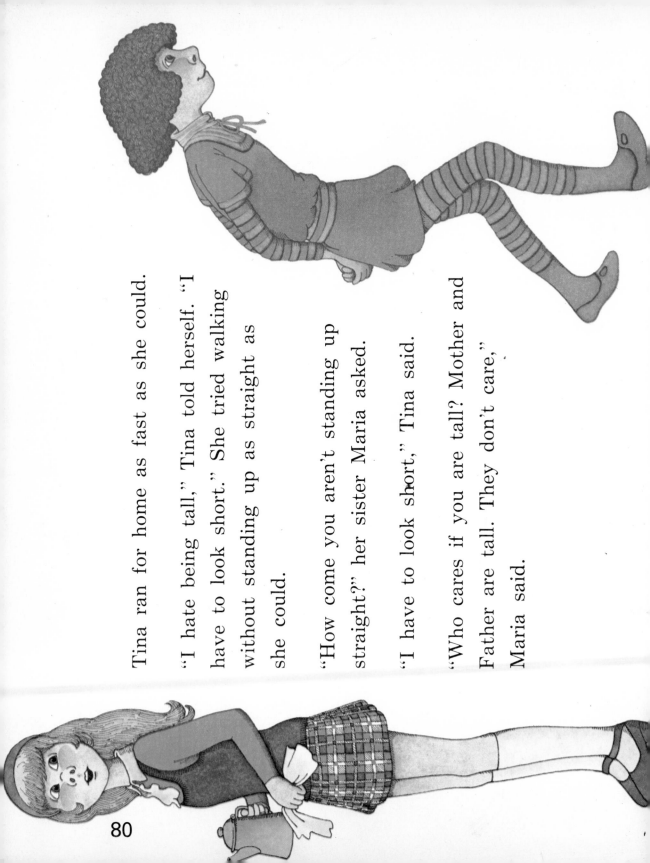

Tina ran for home as fast as she could.

"I hate being tall," Tina told herself. "I have to look short." She tried walking without standing up as straight as she could.

"How come you aren't standing up straight?" her sister Maria asked.

"I have to look short," Tina said.

"Who cares if you are tall? Mother and Father are tall. They don't care," Maria said.

But Tina did care. She couldn't help it. She wanted to look short. She began to think everyone was laughing at her because she was tall. She didn't stand up straight when she was in school.

One afternoon when Tina was walking home, she turned around and saw Rico behind her. She ran as fast as she could for a big fence. She got behind the fence and peeked out.

As Rico came closer, she saw that he was not running after her at all. Two older boys were running after *him!* Then Rico fell, and hit his nose so hard it was bleeding.

While Tina watched, the big boys ran up and laughed at Rico. He had his hand to his nose and tears ran down his face.

"Crybaby!" the boys yelled before they ran off.

Tina stayed behind the fence until the big boys had gone. She was all ready to laugh and say, "Good, Rico! Now you know what it's like to have someone make fun of you."

But, as Tina came over to Rico, she didn't yell at him after all. She was surprised—she felt sorry for Rico! She gave him her handkerchief for his nose.

Slowly he got up. Tina and Rico walked
down the street together without saying
a word.

They stopped at Rico's house.
His nose had stopped bleeding.
Rico gave Tina back her
handkerchief. "Want to see my
new kitten, Tina?" Rico asked.

Tina was surprised again. Rico had never used her right name before, and he wasn't making fun of her. "Maybe he isn't so bad after all," she thought. Still, she wasn't sure she wanted to be his friend.

"My mother is waiting for me," she said. "I'll stop and play with your kitten some other time."

As she walked home, no one called "Tall Tina!" or "String Bean Tina!" That felt good.

Part Three
Tina Runs to Win

A week went by. No one said anything about how tall Tina was. She began to walk straight again.

A warm spring day came, and the children were on the playground. Mr. Peters, one of the teachers, called, "We're going to have races. Rico will be the captain of one team. Kate will be the captain of the other team. Captains, pick your team!"

Kate wanted Joshua for her team. Then Rico had to pick someone. "I take you!" he said, pointing to Tina.

"Why should I be on his team?" Tina asked herself. But she walked slowly over to Rico.

Everyone got on one line or the other. The tall children went to the back of each line. Joshua was the last one on Kate's team. Tina was the last on Rico's team.

"Ready, set, GO!" called Mr. Peters.

Ready, set, GO!

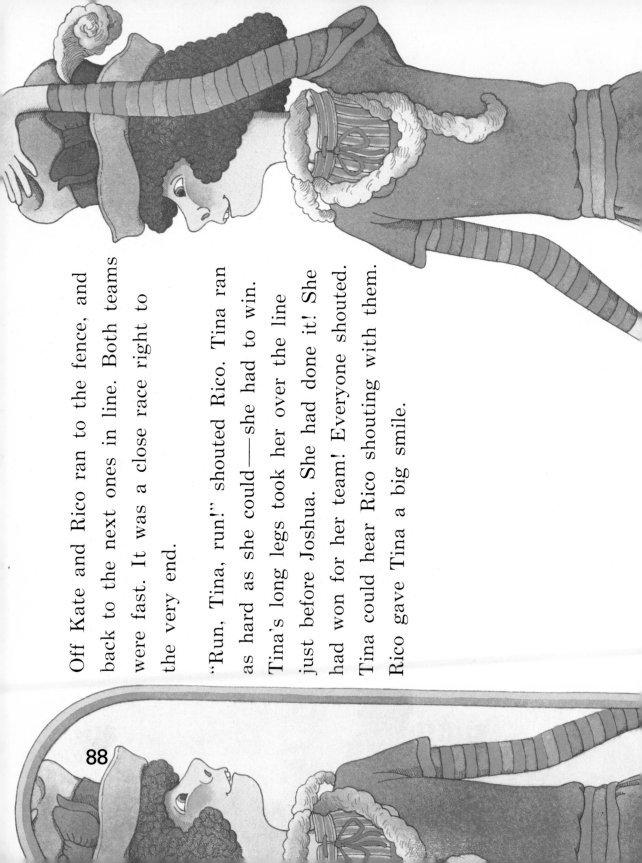

Off Kate and Rico ran to the fence, and back to the next ones in line. Both teams were fast. It was a close race right to the very end.

"Run, Tina, run!" shouted Rico. Tina ran as hard as she could—she had to win. Tina's long legs took her over the line just before Joshua. She had done it! She had won for her team! Everyone shouted. Tina could hear Rico shouting with them. Rico gave Tina a big smile.

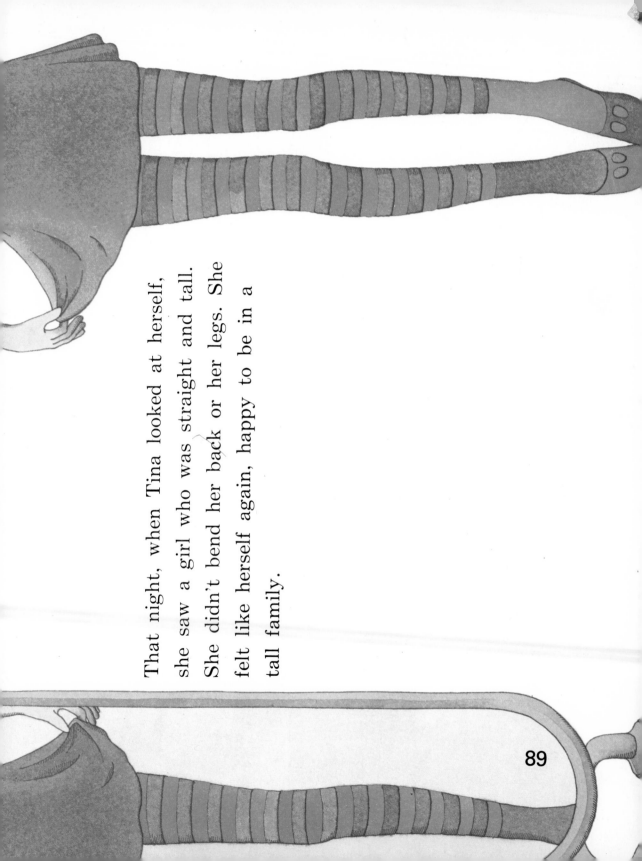

That night, when Tina looked at herself, she saw a girl who was straight and tall. She didn't bend her back or her legs. She felt like herself again, happy to be in a tall family.

89

Who Am I?

The trees ask me,
And the sky,
And the sea asks me
    Who am I?
The grass asks me,
And the sand,
And the rocks ask me
    Who I am.

The wind tells me
At nightfall,
And the rain tells me
Someone small.
Someone small
Someone small
But a piece
of
it
all.

—Felice Holman

81

THE KNEE~HIGH MAN

Julius Lester

Once there was a knee-high man.
He was no taller than a person's knee.
Because he was so tiny, he was very sad.
He wanted to be big like everyone else.

One day he decided to go see
Mr. Horse. "Mr. Horse, how can I get
big like you?" he asked.

Mr. Horse said, "Well, eat a lot of
corn. Then run around a lot. Soon you'll
be as big as me."

So the knee-high man ate so much
corn that his stomach hurt. Then he
ran and ran until his legs hurt. But he
didn't get any bigger. So he decided
that Mr. Horse had been wrong.

He decided to go ask Mr. Bull.
"Mr. Bull, how can I get big like you?"
Mr. Bull said, "Eat a lot of grass.
Then yell and yell as loud as you can.
Soon you'll be as big as me."

So the knee-high man ate so much
grass that his stomach hurt. He yelled
so much that his throat hurt. But he
didn't get any bigger. So he decided
that Mr. Bull was all wrong, too.

Now he didn't know who else to ask.
One night he saw Mr. Hoot Owl, and
he remembered that Mr. Owl knew
everything.

"Mr. Owl, how can I get big like Mr. Horse and Mr. Bull?"

"What do you want to be big for?" Mr. Hoot Owl asked.

"I want to be big so that when I run a race, I will beat everyone."

Mr. Hoot Owl hooted. "Anyone ever try to race with you?"

The knee-high man thought. "Well, now that you ask, no one ever did."

Mr. Owl said, "Then, if you don't have to run races, you don't have to be bigger than you are."

"But Mr. Owl," the knee-high man said, "I want to be big so I can see far ahead of me."

Mr. Hoot Owl hooted. "If you climb a tall tree, you can see far ahead."

"I didn't think of that," said the knee-high man.

Mr. Hoot Owl hooted again. "That's what's wrong, Mr. Knee-High Man. You haven't done any thinking at all. I'm smaller than you, and you don't see me thinking about being big. Mr. Knee-High Man, you wanted something that you don't need."

And the knee-high man knew that Mr. Owl was right.

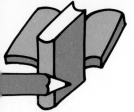

Two Words Can Make One Word

Sometimes two words can go together
to make one word. Look at these words.

---

she + will ⇒ she'll   was + not ⇒ wasn't

he + is ⇒ he's   we + are ⇒ we're

you + have = you've

A. Look at each set of words below.
Make one word out of two words.
Write each new word on your paper.

1. have + not __   1. haven't

2. she + is __   3. you + are __

4. was + not __   5. it + is __

6. can + not __   7. I + will __

8. does + not __   9. what + is __

10. you + will __   11. I + have __

12. that + is __   13. who + is __

14. they + are __   15. could + not __

16. we + will __   17. we + have __

You can also make two words out of one word. Look at these words.

she'll — she will	wasn't — was not
he's — he is	we're — we are
you've — you have	

B. Look at each word below. Make two words out of one word. Write the two words on your paper.

1. you're ___ ___   1. you are
2. aren't ___ ___   3. we've ___ ___
4. he'll ___ ___   5. it's ___ ___
6. I've ___ ___   7. didn't ___ ___
8. won't ___ ___   9. we'll ___ ___
10. that's ___ ___   11. where's ___ ___
12. don't ___ ___   13. doesn't ___ ___
14. they'll ___ ___   15. wouldn't ___ ___
16. can't ___ ___   17. they're ___ ___
18. you'll ___ ___   19. who's ___ ___
20. wasn't ___ ___   21. haven't ___ ___

Gordon the Goat

Munro Leaf

Part One
On the Ranch

Gordon was a goat. He lived on a ranch in Texas. Gordon liked to eat. He didn't care what he ate. He would eat anything. Most of the time he ate leaves from the trees on the ranch. But he was just as happy with an old rag or some ham—if he could get it. Every now and then, Gordon would start to eat a cactus. But he was sorry every time he did!

98

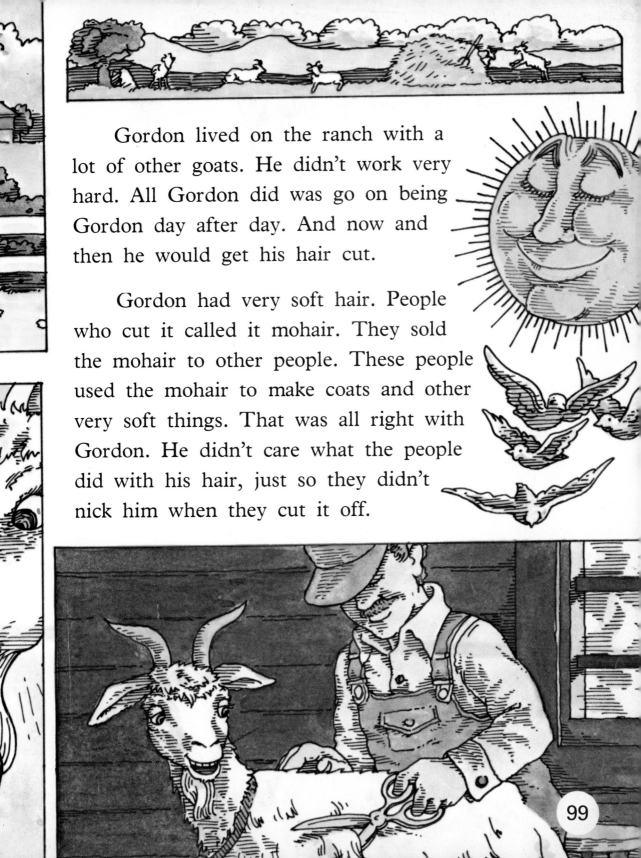

Gordon lived on the ranch with a lot of other goats. He didn't work very hard. All Gordon did was go on being Gordon day after day. And now and then he would get his hair cut.

Gordon had very soft hair. People who cut it called it mohair. They sold the mohair to other people. These people used the mohair to make coats and other very soft things. That was all right with Gordon. He didn't care what the people did with his hair, just so they didn't nick him when they cut it off.

Some of the goats on the ranch were called lead goats. The other goats always walked behind and went every place the lead goats went.

When a lead goat got tired of staying in one place, he would go to another place. All the other goats would tag along behind him.

Sometimes a new place was better than an old place. And sometimes it was not as good. But, better or not, when the lead goat went, all the rest of the goats went along.

Gordon went, too. He didn't know why. He just did what all the rest of the goats did. He didn't really think about it.

But it took Gordon so long to get going that all the other goats were ahead of him. Gordon was always at the tail end of the line.

One hot day, the lead goat got tired of staying where he was, so he started out to find another place. He remembered seeing some new weeds on the other side of a hill. Off he went to find the new weeds. The rest of the goats were right behind him— with Gordon at the tail end of the line.

Part Two
The Twister

After a long, hot walk, the goats found the new weeds. Gordon ate some. The weeds were not very good, and soon Gordon didn't feel very well. He was sorry he had come along. Gordon sat down on the side of the hill. He decided to stay there until he felt better. But just when Gordon was starting to feel a little better, the lead goat went off to look for another place.

Away he went, and the other goats followed him. The very last goat was Gordon, who really didn't feel like going at all.

Gordon walked and walked. The hot sun beat down on him. And Gordon began to ask himself why he was going along. Why didn't he do some thinking for himself? Why had he followed all the other goats, who were following the lead goat just because that was what they always did? It all seemed very silly to Gordon.

Then he saw something way off, ahead of all the goats. It was a big, dark-looking thing. And it was coming right at them. It began right on the ground and it went right up into the sky. Gordon had never seen anything as big before.

The thing was coming at them, faster and faster. Gordon wished that the lead goat would turn around and go another way. But the lead goat went on walking straight ahead. And so the other goats went on walking straight ahead, too.

The thing was coming straight at them until all the goats were right in the middle of it. It was a twister. Now a twister is no fun to be in, and Gordon was scared. Up he flew into the middle of a black cloud. It threw him around and around. It threw him upside down and downside up.

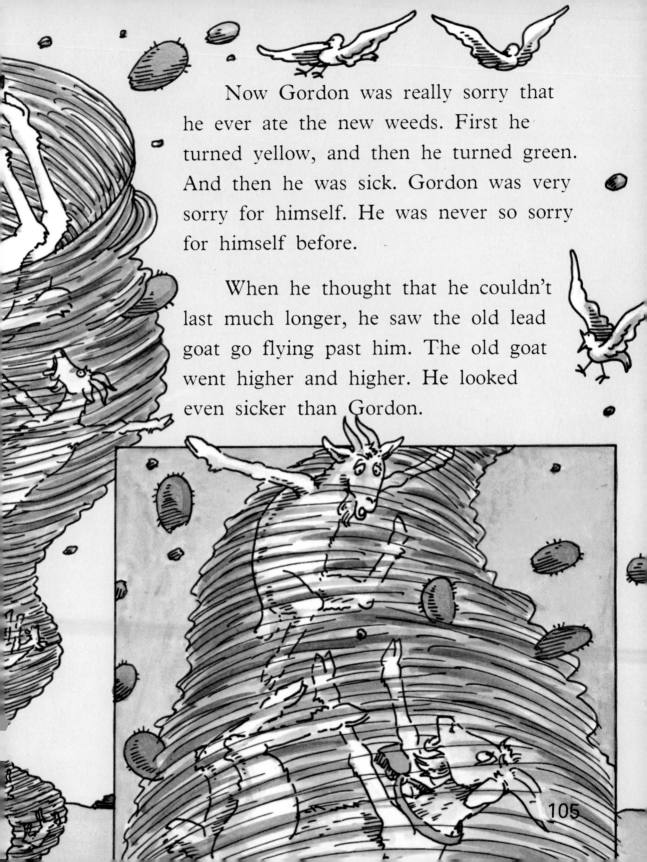

Now Gordon was really sorry that
he ever ate the new weeds. First he
turned yellow, and then he turned green.
And then he was sick. Gordon was very
sorry for himself. He was never so sorry
for himself before.

When he thought that he couldn't
last much longer, he saw the old lead
goat go flying past him. The old goat
went higher and higher. He looked
even sicker than Gordon.

Just then Gordon blew out of the twister. He fell with a bang in the middle of some grass. The grass was soft so he didn't break anything, but still it hurt a lot.

After a long time, Gordon got up. He hurt all over. But Gordon knew something now that he would always remember.

Never again would he follow along
just because all the other goats did.
He was going to find out first—
where he was going,
why he was going, and
what he was going to do
when he got there!

Gordon does his own thinking now.
He gets along much better than before.

UPI

Pittsburgh Athletic Company Inc.

UPI

Roberto Clemente:
The Star From Puerto Rico

Elizabeth Levy

It was the summer of 1971.
Everyone who liked baseball was watching the World Series. Who would win? Not many people thought the Pittsburgh Pirates could win. Only a few fans thought the Pirates could do it. But, by the end of the Series, the Pirates were the winners! How did they do it? They had a star named Roberto Clemente.

Roberto Clemente grew up in Puerto Rico. He always wanted to be a great baseball player. His father thought Roberto should do something better than play baseball. But Roberto didn't give up. He worked hard to become a good ballplayer. Each year he got better and better.

Soon after he got out of school, Roberto Clemente was asked to join the Pittsburgh

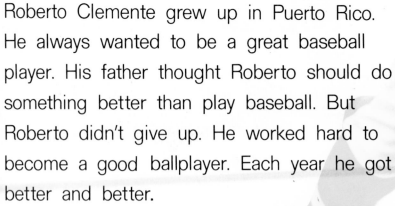

Photo by Les Banos

UPI

UPI

110

Pirates. Once he joined the Pirates, Clemente wanted to show the world that a Puerto Rican could be the best baseball player there was.

It was not always easy for Roberto Clemente to keep playing baseball. In Puerto Rico, his back had been badly hurt when he was hit by a car. One time when he was playing for the Pirates, a ball hit him and hurt his arm. For most of his life, his back and his arm hurt every time he played ball.

But Clemente wouldn't let anything stop him from playing. He had very strong arms and strong hands. He could hit and throw a baseball very well. As the years went by, he became a star player. One year he was named the best player in the league. Four times he was the best batter in the league.

When Roberto Clemente first joined the Pittsburgh Pirates, they were in the last place in their league. But with Clemente's help, they started to win.

In 1971 the Pirates did so well that they got to play in the World Series. Clemente was already a star. But he still wanted to show the whole world that he was the very best player of all.

In the seven games of the World Series, Clemente got on base more than four times out of ten. Nobody did better. He walked up to the plate with his special long bat in his hands. He hit at just about any ball. And nobody did better than Roberto when the Pirates were out in the field. He jumped to catch fly balls as if he had wings. The balls he threw into home plate from the field put many runners out.

The World Series was over. Clemente was the biggest star on the team. He was very happy. He had shown the world that a Puerto Rican was the best in baseball. Roberto Clemente had made Puerto Ricans very proud.

Every winter Roberto went back home
to Puerto Rico. He loved his homeland and
its people. He wanted to help them as much
as he could.

Many times he would be very tired.
All he wanted to do was rest at home
with his wife and sons. But if anyone
asked him for help, he would always say yes.
He went to schools to play baseball
with children. He helped many young
Puerto Rican baseball players get a start.

113

114

UPI

Then in 1972, there was an earthquake in Nicaragua. Many people died, and many more were hurt. Many houses fell down. Many children lost their mothers and fathers in the earthquake. The people in Nicaragua needed help very badly. Roberto got a call for help. At once, he collected a lot of food and money. Then he decided to fly to Nicaragua. He wanted to take the food and money there himself.

UPI

The plane that was taking Roberto Clemente to Nicaragua went down in the ocean. Roberto died. Baseball fans everywhere felt very sad. The whole Pittsburgh Pirates team flew down to Puerto Rico. They wanted to be with Roberto's family. People all over the country said he was not only a great baseball player, but also a very great man. But the people in Puerto Rico felt saddest of all. Roberto Clemente had made them very proud. To them he was a great Puerto Rican.

Not Again

Look at these words. What do they mean?

unhappy — not happy

Un means "not." You can put un in front of a word. Then the meaning of the word changes. Unhappy means "not happy."

Now look at these words. What do they mean?

redraw — draw again

Re means "again." You can put re in front of a word. Then the meaning of the word changes. Redraw means "draw again."

A. Look at each word. Write the word and its meaning on your paper.

    1. unsafe   1. unsafe – not safe

    2. unhurt   **3.** reopen   **4.** retell

    5. untied   **6.** unused   **7.** reread

B. Read each sentence. Look at the underlined word. Write that word and its meaning on your paper.

1. I am <u>undecided</u> as to where I want to go.
   1. undecided — not decided

2. James tried to <u>restart</u> his car.

3. She was <u>unseen</u> behind the door.

4. Alice dropped her money and had to <u>recount</u> it.

5. Father said that another boat was <u>unneeded</u>.

6. The dog jumped on my bed so I had to <u>remake</u> it.

7. These potatoes are <u>uncooked</u>!

8. The letter was <u>unimportant</u> so she threw it away.

9. The new chair was <u>unpainted</u>.

117

The Fastest Quitter in Town

Phyllis Green

Part One
Never a Whole Game

Crack! The girl at bat hit a grounder. A boy in the field got the ball and threw it to Johnny at first base. Johnny thought he had it, but the only thing he had in his glove was...air!

Johnny threw down his glove in disgust. "I quit," he said.

"You always quit when things don't go right," everyone yelled. "Why don't you learn to catch?"

"I can catch. Old Greenly can't throw," Johnny yelled back.

Johnny picked up his glove and ran off the field. When the players couldn't see him any more, he sat down and cried. He had told himself he would play the whole game today, but he had quit right at the start. If only old Greenly could throw a ball right. If only he had not quit right away. Now they would never let him back in the game.

Johnny decided to go and see his great-grandfather. He would tell him all about Greenly's bad throw.

Great-Grandfather lived in the house next door to Johnny's house. He lived with Johnny's grandfather and grandmother. Great-Grandfather was very old. He could not see too well any more, but he was a lot of fun to be with.

When Johnny got there, the first thing Great-Grandfather said was, "Short game today?"

Johnny didn't say anything.

"I thought you were going to play the whole game today. Something go wrong?" asked Great-Grandfather. "Why don't you get some cookies and then tell me about the game?"

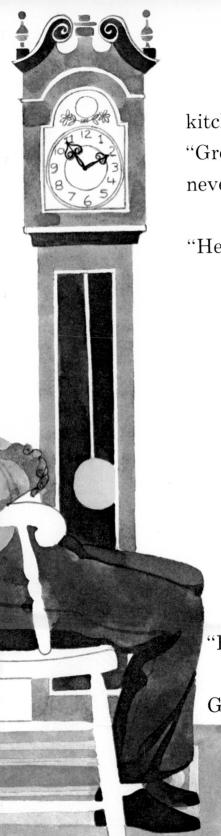

Johnny got some cookies in the kitchen. When he came back, he said, "Greenly thinks he's so hot. Only he never learned to throw a ball."

"That so?" said Great-Grandfather. "He's that bad?"

"He's not really bad," said Johnny. "He just throws a little high."

"A little high for you," said Great-Grandfather.

"Yes," said Johnny.

"Is that why you quit? Because you missed the ball?" asked Great-Grandfather.

"Well, kind of," said Johnny. "But tomorrow I'm going to play the whole game."

Great-Grandfather looked at Johnny. "Tomorrow you'll catch the ball," he said. "But Johnny, even if you don't, don't give up. Stay on the field. It's only a game. You should have fun even if you don't catch the ball."

Part Two
The Lost Ring

The next afternoon Johnny took his glove and walked over to the playground.

"Oh, no," the children said. "Here comes the fastest quitter in town."

Johnny waited by the side of the field and watched the game. Then Greenly called, "Oh, all right, Johnny. We'll let you play. Are you going to play the whole game today?"

"Yes, I am," said Johnny.

"Then get out there and play."

When it was Johnny's turn at bat, he hit the ball way out. It looked like a homer. He ran fast. As he ran, Johnny saw Greenly throwing the ball to the catcher. Johnny ran to home base. He was sure he was safe.

Then everyone yelled, "Out!"

"I'm safe! I'm safe!" Johnny yelled.

"You're out!" they yelled back.

Johnny didn't want to say anything, but the words just came right out. "I quit."

Everyone was disgusted. "This is it for you, Johnny. You're the fastest quitter in town! Don't come around ever again."

"The fastest quitter," said Johnny to himself as he walked away.

Johnny went right over to see his great-grandfather. What would he tell him this time? When he got there, Johnny saw Great-Grandfather sitting in his chair. But he was surprised to see Great-Grandfather looking very sad. Johnny decided not to tell him anything about the game that day.

"Oh, Johnny," said Great-Grandfather. "I need your help. You know my special gold ring—the one I got when I was a boy? Well, I lost it."

"I'll help you find it," said Johnny. "Where do you think you lost it?"

"I don't know," said
Great-Grandfather.

Johnny looked everywhere in the
house. He looked in Great-Grandfather's
chair and in his bed. He looked in all
the rooms. But he didn't find the lost
ring. Great-Grandfather was very sad. He
did not move from his chair. "I have to
find that ring," he said. "I have always
had it on my finger."

"Please don't worry,
Great-Grandfather. You'll get your ring
back. I'll never stop looking for it,"
said Johnny.

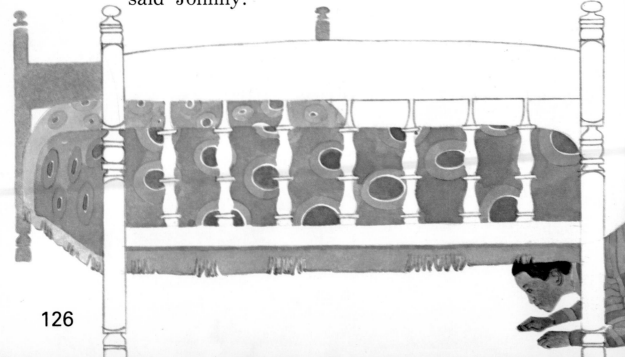

Johnny went over to Great-Grandfather's house the next day and the next. He looked and looked everywhere for the ring. But he couldn't find it.

Each day Great-Grandfather was sadder and quieter. Johnny's grandmother and grandfather began to worry about him. They didn't know what to do.

Then Johnny's grandmother had an idea. "Johnny, I have a ring that looks just like Great-Grandfather's ring. Give him this ring and tell him it's his gold ring."

"But I can't do that," Johnny said. "He'll know. He's smarter than you think. He wants the ring he lost."

"We only want to help Great-Grandfather feel happy again," said his grandmother.

"Oh, all right. I'll give it to him," Johnny said. "But I'm sure he'll know." Johnny went into Great-Grandfather's room and closed the door. He put the ring in Great-Grandfather's hand.

"Johnny, that's not my ring," said Great-Grandfather.

"I know, Great-Grandfather. But I want you to pretend. Grandmother wants you to think that this is your ring so you won't worry so much. Please pretend. I'll never stop looking for your ring. Never."

"Really, Johnny? You won't quit? All right. I'll pretend," said Great-Grandfather.

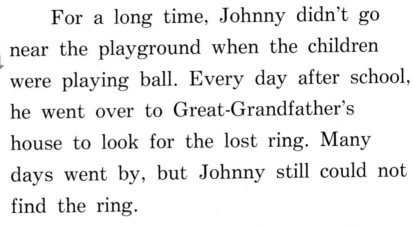

Part Three
Johnny Doesn't Quit

For a long time, Johnny didn't go near the playground when the children were playing ball. Every day after school, he went over to Great-Grandfather's house to look for the lost ring. Many days went by, but Johnny still could not find the ring.

One day Great-Grandfather said, "Johnny, I feel like a little sun today. Help me out to the porch, will you?"

They sat on the porch together, near the yard in back of the house. Great-Grandfather touched the ring on his finger. "Are you still looking for my lost ring, Johnny?"

"Yes, Great-Grandfather, I'm still looking. Please don't give up on me." Then Johnny asked, "Were you out here on the porch the day you lost your ring?"

"I don't know. It's hard to remember," said Great-Grandfather. "But sometimes, when I'm out here, I like to walk in the yard and touch the flowers. I can't see them too well, so I like to touch them."

Johnny had an idea. He ran to the flowers in the yard. He got down on the ground, and began to feel around with his hands. Then he saw something bright. "Oh, please, please, let it be the ring," he thought. He picked up something gold.

"Great-Grandfather,
Great-Grandfather!" he yelled.
"I found it! I found it!"

Johnny ran with the ring to
Great-Grandfather. Great-Grandfather took
the ring and hugged Johnny again and
again. Johnny was very happy. He had
such a good feeling inside. He had not
quit this time. They went in to tell
Grandmother. She put some tape on the
ring so it would not fall off
Great-Grandfather's finger again.

The next day Johnny went over to the playground. All the children laughed when they saw him. "Well, look who's here," they said.

"Can I be in the game?" Johnny asked.

The boy at bat called, "I say **no!** He was kicked out for good."

Other players yelled, "No! He's a quitter."

But then Greenly yelled, "You know we need another player. Get out there, Johnny."

Johnny ran out to take his place in the game. This time he was sure he would not quit. And he didn't. He played the whole game.

It was late that afternoon when Johnny went to see Great-Grandfather.

"Where have you been, Johnny? You're late today. I thought you forgot about me," said Great-Grandfather.

"I was playing baseball," said Johnny. "Great-Grandfather, remember when I was a quitter? Remember when I wouldn't play the whole game? Well, today I didn't quit, and I feel great."

"You, a quitter?" said Great-Grandfather. "I don't remember that at all. That just doesn't seem like you, Johnny."

Johnny took the old man's hand and together they walked out to the yard to look at the flowers.

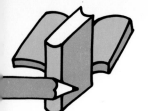

Two Letters Can Stand for One Sound

Say these words. They begin with the same sound.

nurse	knee

The letters n and kn spell the same sound.

Now say these words. They begin with the same sound.

rabbit	write

The letters r and wr spell the same sound.

A. Look at each group of words. Say the words. On your paper, write the words that begin with the same sound.

1. begin   know   now

    1. know   now

2. wrong   river   wood

3. real   knee   nose

4. kiss   night   knew

5.	word	wrote	read
6.	snow	need	knows
7.	name	kick	know
8.	wing	wrote	rock
9.	right	might	write

Say these words. All three words end with the same sound.

boo<u>k</u>	**clo<u>ck</u>**	**wa<u>lk</u>**

The letters <u>k</u>, <u>ck</u>, and <u>lk</u> spell the same end sound.

B. Now look at these groups of words. Say the words. Write on your paper the words that end with the same sound.

1.	talk	sound	peek
2.	block	talk	wrong
3.	wait	cook	walk
4.	shook	baked	talk
5.	week	walk	want

STAND TALL

There are many things you can share
with other people. You can help them
learn new things. You can help them
have fun. They can share with you, too.

Thinking About "Stand Tall"

1. How did Randolph's sister find a way
   to help Randolph learn something new?
2. What did Anita find out that she
   could share with her class?
3. What did Tina find out that she
   could share with Rico?
4. How did Roberto Clemente show that
   he was proud to be himself?
5. What kinds of things can you do that
   you can share with other people?

A SECOND LOOK

Sometimes it can be hard to understand what someone else is saying. No two people think in just the same ways. It can be fun to try to understand the way someone else thinks about the world. You may learn something new.

In "A Second Look," you will read about a family with a magic mirror. You will read about six brothers who don't understand what's wrong. You will read about a boy who thinks everything should be his. As you read, think about the things people do. Why do they do those things?

STICKS, STONES'

Carlos Antonio Llerena Aguirre

A folktale is a make-believe story that people have told and retold for years and years. Long ago, people made up folktales to tell how something came to be. This folktale comes from a country called Peru. Peru is a country in South America.

One day a magic puma from the hills went down into the jungle. The other animals made fun of him. They all had beautiful spots and markings. But the puma had none.

The puma left. He traveled for days. At the top of the mountains, he saw a tree with a bird's nest in it. When Puma grabbed an egg to eat, Father Bird came flying up. He grabbed Puma.

"I will break you in pieces," said Father Bird. Up, up, up he flew with Puma. When Father Bird was very high up, he dropped the puma.

Puma came falling down. He said the magic words to save himself. *"Sticks, stones, change my bones,"* he said. Puma was at once changed into a log. He landed at the side of the mountain.

Lucas, the water carrier, was coming up the road. Lucas had a hole in his fence. He had been looking for just such a log, to fill it. Lucas took the log home and stuck it in his fence.

Puma waited for night to come. When everyone was asleep, he said the magic words. *"Sticks, stones, change my bones,"* he said. He turned himself back into a puma again.

Then he went around to all the farms. He ate all the chickens. In the morning, he changed himself into a log again.

All the farmers found their chickens missing. They were very angry.

"I will make a trap to catch the robber," said Lucas. He went to the waterfall for some sticks. As he looked for the sticks, he heard a voice.

"Help me. I am caught under a stone," called a frog. Lucas ran to free the frog.

"Lucas," said the frog, "the log in your fence is not really a log. It is a magic puma. It changes itself into a puma at night. Then it eats all the chickens. I have seen it."

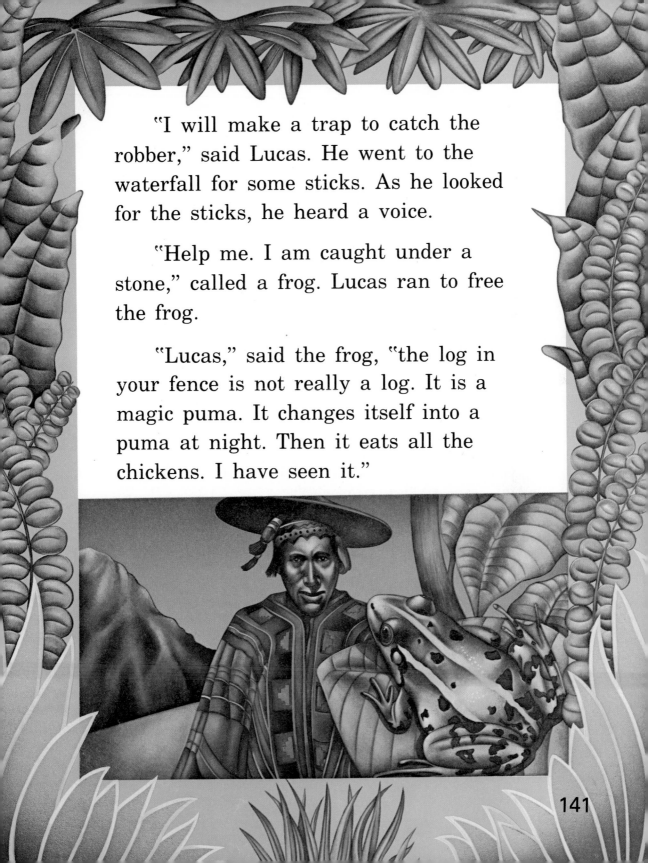

"So!" Lucas said. "If that is how it is, then I know what to do."

Lucas went back home. He put some water in a big pot, as if he were making soup. When the water was very, very hot, he grabbed the log. He threw it into the water.

"Oh!" Puma cried. Quickly he said, *"Sticks, stones, change my bones!"* He changed himself into a puma again. Then he jumped out of the pot. The hot water had turned his fur to gold. And the fire had left beautiful markings on his fur. Puma ran to the jungle.

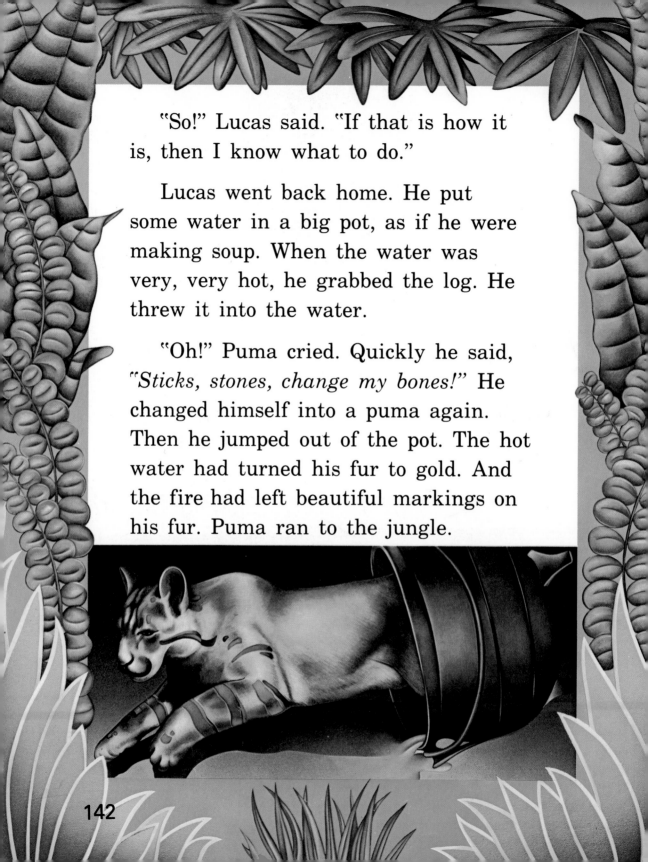

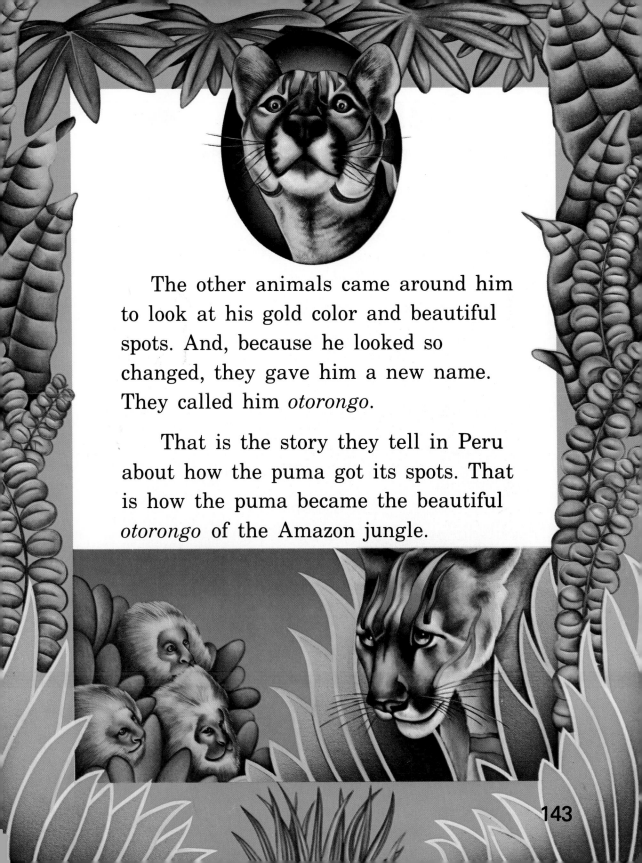

The other animals came around him to look at his gold color and beautiful spots. And, because he looked so changed, they gave him a new name. They called him *otorongo*.

That is the story they tell in Peru about how the puma got its spots. That is how the puma became the beautiful *otorongo* of the Amazon jungle.

The Magic Mirror

Dina Anastasio

Part One
A Wonderful and Very Special Mirror

Mrs. Thomas found the mirror on Friday morning. It was behind a big bed in a shop on John Street, and it didn't take her long to decide to buy it.

"How much?" she asked the storekeeper.

"Ten dollars," he told her.

Mrs. Thomas looked at the mirror. It was very old, and it needed paint badly. "Ten dollars is a lot for something that old," she said.

"But it's special," said the storekeeper, with a smile on his face.

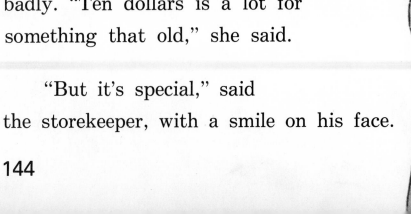

144

"Special? How is it special?"
asked Mrs. Thomas,
looking very puzzled.

"You'll see, you'll see," said
the storekeeper. Mrs. Thomas waited
for the storekeeper to say something
more. But that was all he said
about the mirror.

Mrs. Thomas was more puzzled
than ever. But there was something
about the mirror that made her want
to buy it. She gave the man
ten dollars, and he helped her
carry it to her car.

FOR SALE

On her way home, Mrs. Thomas
stopped at a store for some red paint.
She worked on the mirror for the rest
of the morning. By two o'clock
in the afternoon the paint was dry.
Mrs. Thomas carried the mirror inside
and put it next to the kitchen table.
Then she stood back and stared at it.
It really was a wonderful mirror.

"I'll bet this mirror is
a hundred years old," Mrs. Thomas said
to herself. And she began to think
of all the people who might have owned
it before her. Painters and storytellers
and maybe even a clown or two.

When Ricky and Pam came home,
Mrs. Thomas was still looking
at the mirror.

"Where did you get **that?**"
Ricky laughed.

"That is the most awful thing
I have ever seen!" said Pam.

"I found it in a little shop,"
Mrs. Thomas told them. "And I think
it's wonderful. And very special."

"**Oh, Mother!**" said Pam and
Ricky, and they went out to play.

When Mr. Thomas saw the mirror, he didn't say anything at all. He just stared. Then he went into the living room to read the paper.

But Mrs. Thomas didn't care. She still thought the mirror was wonderful and very special.

Supper that night was **almost** like other nights. Ricky didn't like the beans. Pam didn't like the meat. Mr. Thomas didn't like the milk that fell on the floor. It was **almost** like other nights. The **almost** was the mirror.

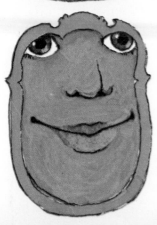

Every time someone shouted
or cried or made a face, the mirror
would show them what they looked like.
They would see how awful or silly or
impossible they looked, and they would
start to laugh.

When Pam said, "I hate this meat!"
she happened to look in the mirror.
She started to laugh. Pam really does
look very funny when she's trying
to be mad. She had just never seen
herself looking mad before.

By the time supper was over,
everyone was happy. Everyone
liked everyone else. That night
the whole family played cards. And no
one screamed or cried or got mad or
anything else. It was very, very nice.

Part Two
A Big Day

The next Friday was to be
a big day for the Thomas family.
Pam was to play a clown
in the school play. Ricky was
to pitch his first baseball game.
Mr. Thomas had to present his
building plan at his office.
And Mrs. Thomas, who had just become
the head of an art school, had
to talk in front of one hundred
very important people.

By Sunday everyone was
nervous. Pam didn't know her lines.
Ricky couldn't get one ball over home plate.
Mr. Thomas wasn't sure what would be
the best way to present his plan. And
Mrs. Thomas couldn't eat, or sleep.
Supper that night was happy again,
because of the mirror. But it was
quieter. No one said very much.
Everyone was thinking about Friday.

That night, after everyone else
had gone to bed, Mrs. Thomas tiptoed
into the kitchen. She turned
on the light and stood in front
of the mirror. She stood as tall
as she could. Then she put her hands
behind her back and smiled
into the mirror. The mirror smiled back.
Mrs. Thomas began to talk. She didn't
talk loudly, for she didn't want
to wake her family. She talked just
loud enough for the woman in the mirror
to hear.

Mrs. Thomas stood before the mirror
all night long. She pretended that it
was Friday and she was talking to one
hundred people. She practiced and
practiced. By the time the sun
came up, she knew that she would be
fine on Friday.

Before she went to bed, she clapped.
And the woman in the mirror
clapped, too.

"You are magic!" said Mrs. Thomas.
She wasn't at all nervous any more.

The next night, when everyone was sound asleep, Mr. Thomas tiptoed out to the kitchen. He turned on the light and stood in front of the mirror. He stood as tall as he could. Then he put his hands behind his back and smiled into the mirror. The mirror smiled back.

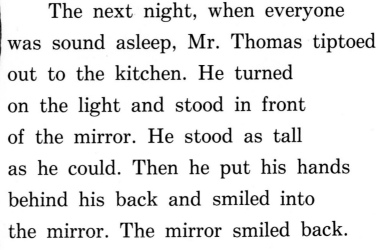

Mr. Thomas took out his papers. He pretended that it was Friday at his office. He talked softly, so as not to wake his family. He practiced all night long. When the sun came up, he knew just what he would say on Friday.

"You are magic!" he said to the mirror. Mr. Thomas was very happy.

The next night, when her mother and father had gone to bed, Pam tiptoed into the kitchen. She had on her clown hat, but when she looked into the mirror, she was still Pam. Pam didn't want to be Pam that night. She wanted to be a clown—a **real** clown.

She pulled herself way, way up, until she was very tall. She put her hands behind her back and made a funny face. Then she smiled at the mirror. And the mirror smiled back. And this time— it was a **real** clown that smiled out of the mirror. It wasn't Pam at all.

Pam practiced her lines all night long. And when the sun came up, she knew her part very well.

Before she went to bed,
Pam stood before the mirror and clapped.
And the clown clapped back at her.

"You are magic!" Pam told
the mirror. She was very happy.

The next night it was Ricky's turn.
When the house was very quiet,
he took out his baseball and bat.
Then he tiptoed into the kitchen
and stood in front of the mirror.
Ricky didn't smile. He just looked grim.
Then he picked up his bat and swung it
behind him. The boy in the mirror
did the same.

Ricky closed his eyes and waited
for the pitcher to throw the ball.

And then he swung.

"**Home run!**" shouted Ricky.

　　Ricky practiced his swing
until two in the morning. When he was
sure that it was just right, he put
his bat on the floor. Then he
picked up his baseball. The boy
in the mirror did the same.
Ricky wound up. His arm flew back.
He closed his eyes and started
to pitch the ball.

　　But he stopped just in time.

"**Strike one!**" shouted Ricky.

Ricky wound up again.
His arm flew back. But again he stopped,
and the ball did not leave his hand.

"**Strike two!**" shouted Ricky.

Ricky wound up once more.
He looked in the mirror, and he saw
a boy. It seemed to Ricky that the boy
was not holding a baseball. He was
holding a bat, and he was waiting
for Ricky to pitch the ball.
Ricky's arm swung back, and

HE THREW THE BALL!

Just as Ricky was about to yell
"Strike three!" a loud cracking noise
sounded throughout the house.
Mr. and Mrs. Thomas ran into the kitchen,
with Pam right behind them.
They stared at the mirror. And they all
understood just what had happened.
Mr. and Mrs. Thomas didn't say
anything. Pam was quiet, too.

Ricky just said, "I got a little
carried away."

And then they all went back to bed.

No one talked to anyone else
the next day. They were all thinking
about Friday. They were all very
nervous. They missed the mirror, but
no one got mad at Ricky. They all
understood what it was like to get
carried away.

159

On Friday morning they met for breakfast.

"I've never been so nervous in my life," said Pam.

"Me, too," everyone said together.

"I can't pitch," Ricky said.

"You did a pretty good job the other night," laughed his father.

"I **was** pretty good, wasn't I?" asked Ricky.

"You were, indeed," said his mother.

"I was **wonderful** in front
of that mirror," said Pam. "I just wish
I could be a clown in front
of the mirror again. That's better
than in front of hundreds of people."

"You're right," said Mr. Thomas.

"Maybe," said Mrs. Thomas, "we can
all pretend that we're in front
of the mirror. Then we'll be as good
as we were before."

And that is just what they did!

The mirror was at Ricky's baseball game.

The mirror was at Pam's play.

The mirror was at Mr. Thomas's office.

The mirror was at
Mrs. Thomas's school.

It smiled.

It clapped.

It looked just like a clown.

And it didn't crack when
Ricky threw strike three!

And everyone was very good indeed!

RAIN POOLS

The rain
litters
the street
with mirror splinters
silver and
brown.

Now
each piece
glitters with

sky
cloud
tree

upside down.

—Lilian Moore

Self-Portraits

Dina Anastasio

A self-portrait is a picture of an artist painted by the artist himself or herself. An artist needs a mirror to draw a self-portrait. On the next few pages you will see what some artists saw when they looked in their mirrors.

Here Norman Rockwell uses a mirror to help him paint a self-portrait. ⟳

This self-portrait was painted in 1498 by Albrecht Dürer when he was 27 years old. ▷

Musee du Louvre, Paris
Photo: F. G. Mayer

Vincent van Gogh painted many self-portraits during his lifetime. This one, painted in 1890, was his last. ◁

Musee du Louvre, Paris

This self-portrait, by Leonardo da Vinci, was made about 1510. The artist used red chalk to give a feeling of age to the drawing. ◁

Armeria Reale, Turin

Malvin Gray Johnson painted this self-portrait when he was a young man. Behind the artist you can see one of his other paintings. ▷

Smithsonian Institution

Artists sometimes use pictures in place of
mirrors. Gwendolyn Smith, age 7½, is using
the picture in the corner as a mirror of
herself.

Artists have been looking in mirrors and drawing self-portraits for hundreds of years. This is how Everett Kelsey, age 8, drew himself.

New Friends

Judith Davis

Part One
Playing Checkers

I like to make things with my dad.
Last week, we made a checker game for
me. The checkers go into holes, so I won't
knock them off with my arm. My left arm
doesn't work very well. It doesn't always do
what I want it to do. Sometimes I reach for
a checker and miss it.

Sometimes I get mad at my arm. I say, "This arm is no good at all!" Then my mom calls my arm a lot of funny names. I laugh at the names and then work with my arm some more. I know I should use my left arm as much as I can. If I do, I can do more things with two arms.

That's why Dad and I made the checker game. It helped me practice using my arm. We painted the board red and black. It really looked good.

I took my checker game to school. I showed it to my teacher, Mrs. Bell. She said, "What a good job, Ginny!"

"I'm going to use it for the contest," I told her. We are going to have a checkers contest in school soon. I hope I win.

There was a new girl standing next to Mrs. Bell. She looked at my game. But she didn't say anything.

"Ginny," said Mrs. Bell. "This is Miyoko. She's going to be in our class from now on."

"Hi, Miyoko," I said.

Miyoko didn't say anything. She just looked down at the floor. In fact, Miyoko didn't say anything all day. When Mrs. Bell called on her, she always looked down at the floor.

The next day, my friend Debbie tried to talk to Miyoko about the contest. "Do you want to play checkers after lunch?" she asked. Miyoko just shook her head.

Later, I went over to her. "Do you know how to play checkers?" I asked. Miyoko shook her head and looked down at the floor.

175

"I can show you how," I told her. "Mrs. Bell showed all of us how. We can use the board I made with my dad."

Miyoko didn't say anything. But she picked up a red checker. "You can have the reds," I said.

Miyoko sat down across from me. I showed her how to play. Then we played a few games. Miyoko did very well.

"You've got the idea," I said. But she still didn't say anything.

"Can't you talk?" I asked.

"Sure, I can talk!" said Miyoko.

"Then how come you never talk to any of us?" I asked.

After a minute, Miyoko said, "I don't know anybody."

"You know me now," I said. "You have to talk to people. That's how you get to know them."

"But I don't have any friends here," said Miyoko.

"You can be one of my friends," I said.

Miyoko smiled. It was a really nice smile. "Do you want to play another game?" she asked.

"Sure," I said.

Miyoko and I played checkers the next day, too. I had to try very hard to win.

"You are getting better and better," I told her.

"Thanks, Ginny," she said.

Then I reached over the board to pick up a checker. My arm knocked it off. Miyoko picked it up for me. She didn't laugh.

"Why doesn't your arm work very well?" she asked.

"It just came that way," I said. "But the more I use it, the more things I can learn to do with it. And that means I can get to do more things with two arms."

"What is that on your leg?" Miyoko asked.

"It's a brace," I said. Everyone always
wants to know that.

"What is it for?" Miyoko asked.

"It holds my foot up in the right place,
so I won't fall over it."

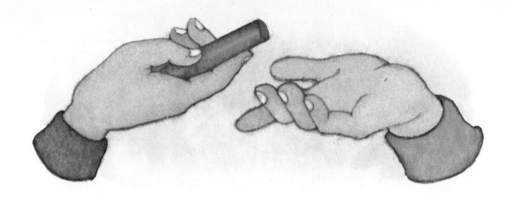

"Does it hurt?" Miyoko wanted to know.

"No," I said. "But sometimes I get tired of it."

"Do you sleep with the brace on?"

"Oh no! I take it off at home a lot. I have to use my leg as much as I can, too. Come on, let's play another game."

"Okay," said Miyoko. She looked at me. Then she said, "You sure have a lot to do."

We played another game. Then we went over to talk to Debbie and Linda and Kay.

Part Two
The Contest

Miyoko and I played checkers every day. It got harder and harder for me to beat her. Then, one day, Miyoko won a game.

"You're really getting good, Miyoko," I said. "It's awfully hard to beat you."

"Thanks, Ginny," said Miyoko. "I like playing with you. It's fun."

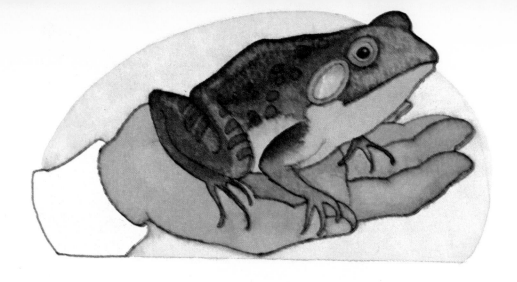

Miyoko and I talked often now. I told her about Funny Fred, my frog. I told her about the bird's egg I found in the grass. I also told her about the secret place in my house. "Someday soon you should come and see my secret place," I said.

Miyoko told me about the bread she knows how to bake. She told me about the mice she found in a field. She told me about her giant kite, too. It looks like a great big butterfly. "Someday soon you can come and bake bread with me," she said. "Then we'll fly my kite."

That day, Miyoko talked to Debbie and Linda and Kay again. She even started talking to lots of other people in our class.

Miyoko and I kept on playing checkers every day, too. We played checkers right up until the day of the contest. Sometimes I won. Sometimes she won.

Miyoko was a good player now. She was really good. But I was just as good as she was. I was sure I could win the contest.

On the day of the contest, I played Ben and then Linda. I won both games. Miyoko played Raul and then Kim. She won both games, too.

We kept on playing until Miyoko and I had won the most games. Then she and I had to play the last game to see who would win the contest.

"Good luck, girls," said Mrs. Bell. "You're both good players."

It was a hard game. It took a long time. Everyone in the class watched us. Finally, just when I thought I was going to win, Miyoko jumped my king. She won the game! Miyoko won! Everyone clapped.

I couldn't believe it. I was sure I was going to win!

"Quiet, everyone," Mrs. Bell said. "Miyoko is the winner of the contest. Congratulations, Miyoko. You played very well."

Miyoko came and stood next to me. I didn't look at her. "Listen, Ginny," she said. "You're still the best player I know." She gave me a hug.

This time, I was the one who didn't say anything. I wanted to cry. But I didn't want anyone to see my tears.

Then Mrs. Bell surprised me. "We have another very good player here," she said. "She is also a very good friend. She helped Miyoko feel at home here. She taught her how to play checkers. In fact, she taught Miyoko so well that now we have *two* very good players. Congratulations to Ginny who is good at many things—even when there isn't a contest."

Everyone clapped again.

"You might be the winner next time," Miyoko said.

"I know," I said. It's funny how you can feel good and bad at the same time.

"We can still play checkers after lunch too," said Miyoko.

"I know," I said again. I didn't feel so bad then. I even felt pretty good.

"You can even show me Funny Fred and your secret place," Miyoko said.

"You bet," I said. I looked at Miyoko and smiled. Now I felt just great! "And you can show me how to bake bread and fly your kite."

And that's how it was.

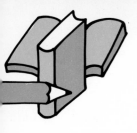

How Many Are There?

Some words tell about more than
one thing. They end in _-s_ or _-es_.
Look at each picture. Read the words
below the pictures.

one tree

two tree<u>s</u>

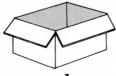

one box

three box<u>es</u>

A. Look at each picture. Choose
the sentence that tells what is in
the picture. Write the correct
sentence on your paper.

1.

There is a letter.
There are many letters.

1. There are many letters.

188

2.  There is a sandwich.
There are many sandwiches.

3. There is a hand.
There are many hands.

4. There is a branch.
There are many branches.

B. Read each part of a sentence.
Choose the correct word to finish
the sentence. Write the whole
sentence on your paper.

1. This new _dress_ is Rachel's.
(dress   dresses)

2. Fred told us lots of baseball ____ .
(story   stories)

3. Miyoko takes two ____ to get to school.
(bus   buses)

4. Myra made a birthday ____ for Raul.
(cake   cakes)

5. Mrs. Perez has many ____ in her window.
(plant   plants)

The Ghost Catcher
A Tale from India

Now this is a very old story from India. It is about a young barber who did not really want to be a barber. And it is about a ghost—two ghosts.

The young barber's name was Ved. Ved didn't like being a barber. He didn't like cutting hair or shaving faces. He really wanted to be a farmer.

But Ved's father was a barber. And when Ved's father died, all he left his son was his bag of barber tools— razors, brushes, combs, and a mirror. So what could Ved do? He tried to be a barber, too. In those days, you had to do whatever your father did.

Well, Ved was a clever boy, but he wasn't a good barber. And after a while people stopped coming to him.

"He's not as good a barber as his father," they said.

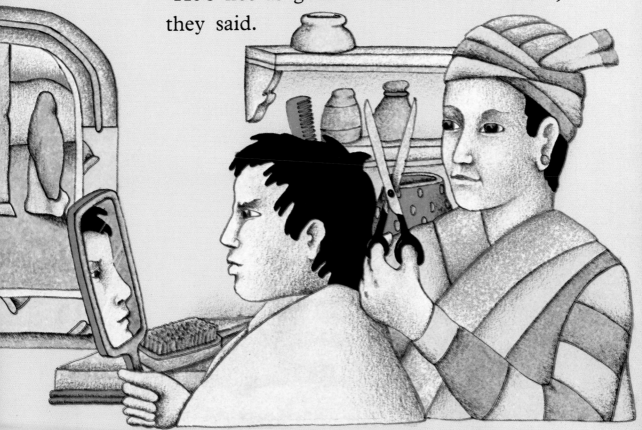

"I'd rather be a farmer," Ved thought. "But if I have to be a barber, I will leave this town. I will go to the city. There no one will know that my father was a better barber than I."

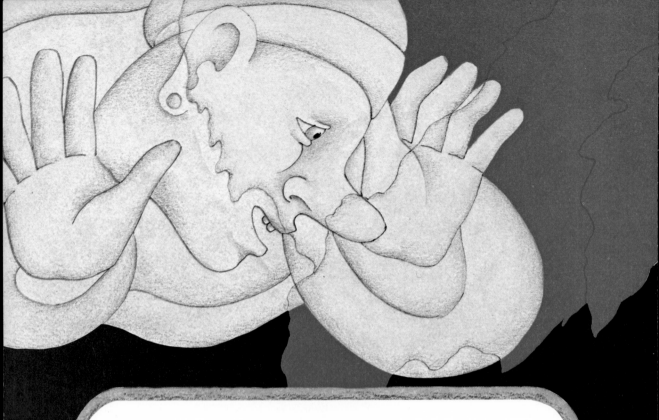

And so Ved picked up his bag of barber tools—razors, brushes, combs, and a mirror. He set off for the city.

Ved walked all morning and he walked all afternoon. When night came, Ved sat under a willow tree to rest. The city was still a long way off. So Ved decided to spend the night under the willow tree. "Then I can start out fresh in the morning," he said to himself. Ved lay down on the ground and fell asleep at once.

As luck would have it, that very willow tree was haunted by a ghost. Soon after Ved fell asleep, the ghost floated down from the treetop crying, "BOOOOOOO!"

Ved woke up at once. "What a bad dream," he said to himself. "I dreamed this willow tree was haunted by a ghost."

"BOOOOOOO!" cried the ghost again. Now it was right at Ved's ear. This was not a dream! Ved had to think fast.

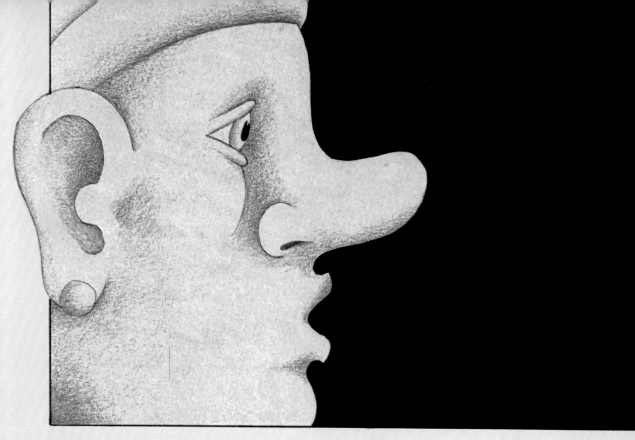

"Don't you come close to me, ghost,"
Ved said quickly. "D-Do you know what
I am? I-I'm a GHOST CATCHER!
That's what I am! I catch ghosts and
put them in my ghost bag."

And with that Ved opened his bag
of barber tools and pulled up the mirror.
"Here, let me show you one ghost
I've caught tonight," he said. Ved held
the mirror up to the ghost's face.
"I think I'll put you in the bag, too."

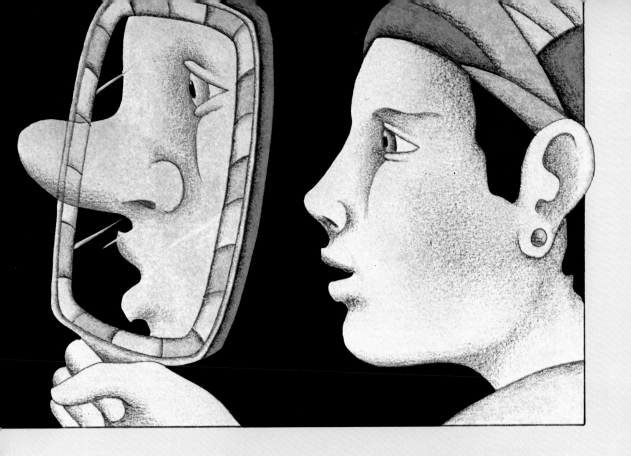

The ghost looked into the mirror—and
what did it see? Its own face, of course.
But the ghost didn't know that. It thought
the barber really had caught a ghost
in the bag.

"Oh, please," said the ghost, "don't
put me in your ghost bag. I'll give
you anything you want. Just let me go."

"Anything I want?" said Ved. "Then I
want a bag of gold. Maybe two bags."

Zip! In a second two bags of gold were at Ved's feet.

"Good enough," Ved said. "I won't put you in my bag this time. But remember, if you bother me again, into the ghost bag you go." As soon as Ved let the mirror fall back into the bag, the ghost was gone.

Ved never did go to the city. He took some of the gold the ghost had given him and he bought himself a farm. He bought cows and pigs and horses. Ved was a fine farmer. He didn't have to cut hair or shave faces any more. But Ved kept his bag of tools—and that was very clever of him.

For, as luck would have it, the ghost
met a friend one day and told the friend
everything that had happened.
At the end of the story, the friend
laughed and laughed.
"Hoo, hoo, hoo," the friend laughed. "No
one can catch a ghost. And there is no
such thing as a ghost bag. You have
been tricked."

"Well, go and see for yourself,"
the ghost said. "But don't be angry
at me if that man puts you in his bag."

The friend floated over to Ved's house
and peeked through the window.

Ved was eating his supper. He felt
a cold wind and looked up. Another
ghost! Ved ran to get his bag of tools.
Quickly, he opened the bag and pulled
out the mirror. Then he held the mirror
up on the window and shouted, "Come
on in! I'll put you in the bag, too!"

The friend took one look at the ghost
in the mirror and floated off as fast as
it could go.

From that time on, no ghost ever dared
to bother Ved again. But Ved was clever
enough to keep his bag of barber tools
handy. But he never had to use
them again.

That's a Fact

Look at the picture. Read the sentence below the picture.

Five frogs are on the rock.

This sentence is a fact. It is true. You can prove it. How many frogs are in the picture? Where are the frogs? Five frogs *are* on the rock.

Read this sentence.

Frogs are the most beautiful animals in the world!

This sentence is *not* a fact. You cannot prove it. It is what someone thinks or believes.

Read each sentence. On your paper,
write the sentence that is a fact.

1. Walking this big dog is fun.
   Betsy took her dog for a long walk.
   1. Betsy took her dog for a long walk.

2. "The Magic Mirror" is a story
   in this book.
   "The Magic Mirror" is the best
   story I ever read.

3. Eugene ate three eggs for breakfast.
   Eggs are the only things to eat
   for breakfast.

4. Maria made a birthday present for Bob.
   Maria's birthday present is the best
   one of all.

5. Uncle Henry has the biggest boat
   in the world.
   Uncle Henry has a big boat that sailed
   across the lake.

I Don't Know Why

I don't know why
    the sky is blue
    or why the raindrops
    splatter through

    or why the grass
    is wet with dew . . . do you?

I don't know why
    the sun is round
    or why a seed grows
    in the ground

    or why the thunder
    makes a sound . . . do you?

I don't know why
    the clouds are white
    or why the moon
    shines very bright

    or why the air
    turns black at night . . . do you?

Myra Cohn Livingston

202

203

Five in a Pod

Hans Christian Andersen

There lived five peas in one pod. The peas were green and the pod was green so they thought the whole world was green. The pod grew and the peas grew. They made themselves as cozy as they could and sat close together in a row. The sun warmed the pod, and the rain made it nice and clean. It was quite cozy, there in the pod. And the peas sat growing bigger and bigger.

At last one pea said, "Are we to sit here forever? We'll all get backaches from too much sitting in one place. I have an idea that something is going on outside. It's just a feeling I have."

Weeks went by. The pod turned yellow and the peas turned yellow. "The whole world is turning yellow," they said. And they had every right to say so.

All at once they felt a pull at the pod. The pod was broken off and held a second in a boy's hand. Then it was pushed into a coat pocket.

"It won't be long now before we're out in the world," said the peas. And they could hardly wait until the time came.

"I wonder which of us will become the most remarkable," said the smallest of the five. "Well, we'll soon find out."

Pop! The pod opened and all five peas came rolling out into the bright sunshine. The boy looked at them. The peas were just what he needed for his peashooter. He put one of the peas into the peashooter and let it go.

"Here I go," cried the pea, "flying out into the wide world! Catch me if you can." And he was gone.

"I," yelled the second, "shall show everyone how far I can go!" And away he went.

The next two were lazy. They said, "We'll get wherever we're going. It won't make any difference *what* we do. So we'll just keep rolling along." But they were not rolling very long. They got into the peashooter just the same.

Soon it was time for the last one. "What will be, will be," said the last as he went flying out of the peashooter. He flew up to an old board under an attic window. He landed in a crack filled with some moss and soft earth. There he lay, alone, and hidden by the moss—forgotten by all.

"What will be, will be," he said.

In the attic lived a poor woman and her little daughter. The mother went out to work every day. She did all kinds of hard work. But she was still as poor as ever.

At home in the attic was her only child, the little daughter, who had been sick for a whole year. She showed no signs of getting better. Sadly the mother thought her child would never get well. All day long the sick girl lay in her bed quietly, while her mother was away at work.

One spring morning the mother was about to leave for work. Just then the sun came through the window. The sick child turned her eyes to the window.

"Mother, there's a little green thing looking in at the window," she said. "See, it's moving in the wind. What can it be?"

The mother went to the window and opened it a little. "Why, it's a tiny plant," she said. "A pea plant. It's taken root and has pushed up its green leaves. How did it ever find its way here? There, now you have something pretty to look at."

She moved the child's bed nearer to the window. Then she went off to work.

Later that day when the mother came back, the little girl looked very happy. "Mother, I believe I'm going to get well," she said. "All day long the sun has been shining on the little plant. It's coming along fine—and so am I. I know I'll be able to get up soon. It would be so nice to go out into the sunshine again."

"That would be so wonderful!" said the mother. But she really did not believe such a thing could happen. Still, she was thankful to the little plant that had made her sick child so happy. So she took a little stick and put it up right next to the plant. Then she tied a piece of string from the window sill to the upper part of the window. Now the little pea had somewhere to climb.

"Oh, look," cried the mother one morning, "our little plant has a flower!" And now she dared hope that her sick child would get well at last.

211

About a week later, the child was able to
get up for the first time. She sat for a whole
hour in the warm sunshine. The window was
wide open. And there outside stood a pea
flower in full bloom. The little girl leaned
over and softly kissed the flower.

"This is a day of great joy," said the happy
mother. And she smiled at the pea plant as
if to say *thank you.*

Well, and now—what about the other peas? The first one, who went flying out into the wide world crying, "Catch me if you can!" landed on a rooftop. Soon a bird caught him and ate him up. The lazy two met with another bird, who made short work of them also. The one who was going to show everyone how far he could go ended up in a garbage can. He lay there in the water getting bigger and bigger. "How big and round I'm getting," he said. "In no time I will be the fattest and roundest pea around. I believe I'm the most remarkable of the five out of our pod."

But at the attic window stood the little girl, her eyes bright and shining. She was looking at the pretty pea plant. Its fresh green shoots were beginning to climb all over her window.

What Someone Said
When He Was Spanked
On The Day Before
His Birthday

Some day
I may
Pack my bag and run away.
Some day
I may.
—But not today.

Some night
I might
Slip away in the moonlight.
I might.
Some night.
—But not tonight.

Some night.
Some day.
I might.
I may.
—But right now I think I'll stay.

—*John Ciardi*

214

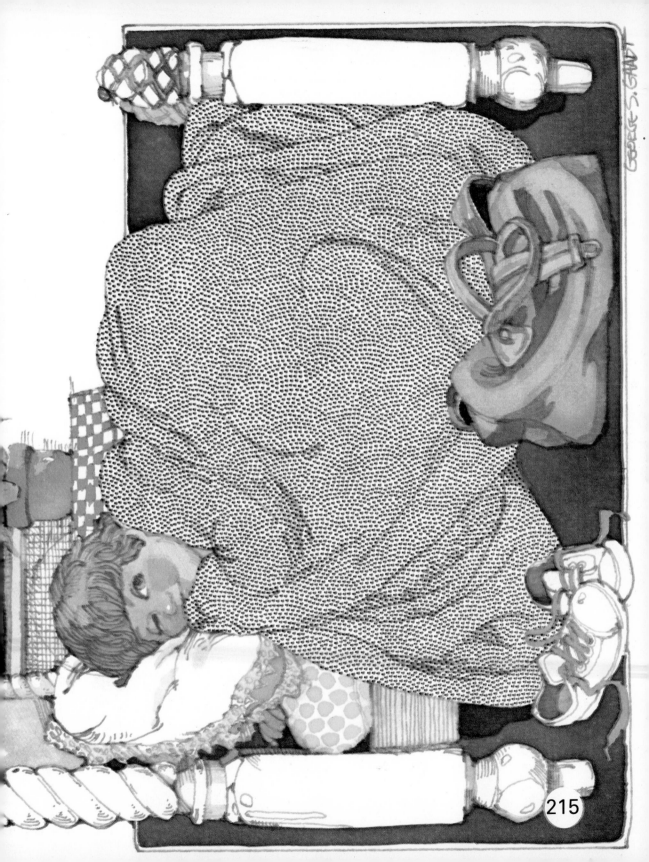

215

This is a play about a girl and six foolish brothers who are fishers. Because the fishers are men, it does not mean that only boys can play their parts. Long ago, men played the parts of women in all plays. And women often played the parts of men. The parts in *The Six Foolish Fishermen* may be played by either boys or girls.

The Players

THE SIX FOOLISH FISHERMEN

Benjamin Elkin

Storyteller

First Brother

Third

Second

Brother

Sixth Brother

Fifth Brother

Fourth Brother

Brother

Girl

217

Storyteller: Once there were six brothers who decided to go fishing. So they went to the river and picked good spots to rest and fish.

First Brother: I will sit in this boat.

Second Brother: And I will kneel on this raft.

Third Brother: And I will lean on this log.

Fourth Brother: And I will stand on this bridge.

Fifth Brother: And I will lie on this rock.

Sixth Brother: And I will walk on this bank.

Storyteller: And that is just what they did. Each brother fished from the spot he had picked. And each one had good luck. But when it was time to go home, the brothers became a little nervous.

First Brother: We have been near the river, and over the river, and on the river. Maybe one of us fell into the river and was drowned. I shall count all the brothers to be sure there are six of us.

Storyteller: And he began to count.

First Brother: *(counting his brothers)*
    I see one brother on the raft.
    That's **one.**
    And another on the log.
    That's **two.**
    And another on the bridge.
    That's **three.**
    And another on the rock.
    That's **four.**
    And another on the bank.
    That's **five.**
    Only **five!**
    Oh, dear me!
    We have lost a brother!

Second Brother: Can it really be?
    Has one of us been drowned?
    And have we really lost a brother?

Storyteller: And he, too, began to count.

Second Brother: I see one brother on the log.

That's **one.**

And another on the bridge.

That's **two.**

And another on the rock.

That's **three.**

And another on the bank.

That's **four.**

And another in the boat.

That's **five.**

Only **five!**

What will our dear mother say?

221

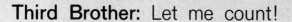

Third Brother: Let me count!

I see one brother on the bridge.

That's **one**.

And another on the rock.

That's **two**.

And another on the bank.

That's **three**.

And another in the boat.

That's **four**.

And another on the raft.

That's **five**.

Five in all! Oh, unhappy day!

Why did we ever come here for one of us

to be drowned!

Storyteller: Then the fourth brother counted,

and the fifth and the sixth.

(The brothers run around counting.)

223

Storyteller: Each one counted only five brothers. All the brothers went back to the river and ran sadly up and down the side of the river, trying to see if they could see their poor drowned brother in the water. Then along came a girl. The girl had been fishing, too. But she had not been able to catch any fish at all.

Girl: What's the matter? You have a lot of fish. Why do you all look so sad?

Fourth Brother: Because six of us came here to fish, and now there are only five of us left. One of our dear brothers has been drowned!

Girl: What do you mean, only five left? How did you get that?

Fifth Brother: Look, I'll show you. *(points to his brothers)* One...Two...Three...Four...Five... Six of us came here and now only five are going back. Sad is the day!

Storyteller: The girl turned to hide her smile, and then she turned back.

Girl: I think I can help you find your lost brother. When I squeeze your hand, I want you to count.

Storyteller: As hard as she could, she squeezed the hand of each of the brothers in turn.

First Brother: *(yelling as Girl squeezes his hand)* ONE!

Second Brother: *(crying and jumping up and down because of the hard squeeze)* TWO!

Third Brother: THREE!

Fourth Brother: FOUR!

Fifth Brother: FIVE!

Sixth Brother: SIX!

Storyteller: SIX! The brothers looked at each other in surprise. There were six of them again! They jumped for joy and hit each other on the back. And they turned to the girl.

Sixth Brother: Here, take all our fish. We can never thank you enough for finding our dear lost brother.

Storyteller: So the girl took the fish. And the six foolish fishermen went home.

227

THE DOG AND THE BONE

Aesop

One day a dog, carrying a bone in his mouth, was walking over a big river.

Looking down from the bridge, he saw his own reflection in the water. But he thought it was another dog.

He began to bark, for he was greedy for the other's bone. As soon as he opened his mouth, his own bone fell into the water. And it was lost forever.

A Thought:

It is better to take care
of your own things
than to be greedy
for those of others.

Fun With Fables

The story you have just read called "The Dog and the Bone" is a fable. A fable is a very short story. Fables are nearly always about animals, but they teach something that people can learn. Here is another fable by Aesop.

 Once a big lion was taking a nap. A little mouse ran over his foot and woke him up. "You will be my dinner!" roared the angry lion.

"Oh, please let me go," cried the mouse. "Someday I can help you."

"You are too little to help me," laughed the lion. But he let the mouse go.

Later, the mouse heard the lion roaring. She ran to see what was wrong and found the lion tied in a rope. Quickly she set to work and soon had the rope off the lion.

"Thank you, little mouse," said the lion. "Now I see that what you said was right. Little friends are as important as big friends."

What to Do

Pick one of the two fables you have read. With a friend, plan a puppet play about the fable. Make a puppet for each animal. You and your friend can move the puppets and say the words. Practice your play. Then do it for your class and your teacher.

A big paper bag makes a lion.

A mitten makes a dog.

Bone

A small paper bag makes a mouse.

your fingers

Dick Thompson— The Selfish Boy

Betty MacDonald

Part One
Mine! Mine! Mine!

Dick Thompson was a very nice-looking boy, and he was smart in school. But whenever his name came up, people said, "Poor, poor Mrs. Thompson. She has such a problem. Whatever will she do with that boy?"

I'll bet you would feel just awful if people said a thing like that when your name came up. But Dick didn't. You see, Dick Thompson was a selfish, greedy boy. And he cared more about being a selfish, greedy boy than about what people said.

When children came over to his house to play, Dick said, "Don't touch that, that's **mine!** You can't play with that, that's **mine!** Put down **my** ball. Take off **my** hat!"

232

Each time his mother heard him
say this, she would send him up
to his room to think about how selfish
he was. Dick would go right up, for he
always did what his mother told him.
But he didn't think about how selfish
he was. He just sat on the bed and
swung his legs and thought, "Everything
in this room is **mine**. No one is going
to touch **my** things!"

233

He sure was a problem.

One day Dick's mother bought
a big box of peppermint sticks.
She called Dick into the house and said,
"Now, dear, I have bought this big box
of peppermint sticks for you. But I want
you to share them with your friends.
Don't forget the little children, Dick, and
you might take some to the woman
next door. She loves peppermint."

Dick said, "Thank you, Mother,
for the fine candy." Then he took the box
outside and put it in the basket on the
front of his bike. He let the other
children look at his peppermint sticks.
But he told them, "This is **my** candy
and nobody can touch it!"

The children knew Dick very well.
They understood that he would do
something if they touched his candy.
But, as they looked at the candy, they
wished and wished that they could have
just one stick. Dick's mother, watching
from the window, saw all the children
gathered around Dick. She saw the box
of candy in the basket on the front
of his bike.

"Just look at Dick," she
thought to herself. "He's going to
divide the candy with all his little
friends. I just knew he would learn
to share." And she waved and smiled
at Dick.

Dick waved and smiled back. But
just then Kim James, who wasn't afraid
of anything, took a stick of candy.
CRACK! Dick hit her on the hand.

And it was then that his mother saw what was going on. She flew out the front door, took Dick by the arm, and marched him up to his room. Then she took the box of candy and told Kim to give some to all the children.

From the window of his bedroom, Dick watched Kim divide the candy. He was very mad.

After all the candy had been divided, Mrs. Thompson went into the house and called Dick's father. She said, "Leroy, we have a problem. I'm so unhappy about Dick."

Dick's father said, "What is the matter? Is he sick?"

Dick's mother said, "No, but I wish he were. Then it would be so easy." And she told him about the peppermint sticks.

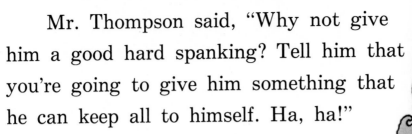

Mr. Thompson said, "Why not give him a good hard spanking? Tell him that you're going to give him something that he can keep all to himself. Ha, ha!"

"Now, Leroy," said Mrs. Thompson. "This is not a laughing matter. I don't think a spanking will help at all. I just don't know what to do or where to turn."

Dick's father said, "I know. I know just what to do. Call that Mrs. Wiggle-Piggle or whatever her name is. You know, the one who cured Butch Brown."

"You mean Mrs. Piggle-Wiggle. Oh, Leroy, you are so wonderful! I'll call her right away," said Mrs. Thompson. She was already beginning to smile.

Part Two
Mrs. Piggle-Wiggle

Mothers always do cheer up when they think of Mrs. Piggle-Wiggle because she knows so much about children. After all, she has had about nine hundred little boys and girls come to her house. They would bake cookies, play cards, have tea, and dig for gold in her backyard. She was just the one to ask about Dick, the selfish boy. So Mrs. Thompson called her. She said, "Hello, Mrs. Piggle-Wiggle. This is Mrs. Thompson, Dick's mother."

Mrs. Piggle-Wiggle said, "Hello, Mrs. Thompson. I have been waiting for your call."

Mrs. Thompson said, "You have? Why?"

"Because I know Dick very well," said Mrs. Piggle-Wiggle. "Dick is a dear boy, but he is very selfish."

"Oh, I know he is. I know he is," said Mrs. Thompson. She was just about to cry because Mrs. Piggle-Wiggle knew how selfish Dick was.

Mrs. Piggle-Wiggle said, "Now Mrs. Thompson, don't feel sad. Selfishness is just like a cold. It's very easy to cure. But we must start now, before another day goes by. Dick is such a nice little boy. We want everyone to like him as we do."

"Oh, do you like him, even if he's selfish?" asked Dick's mother.

"Yes—I do," said Mrs. Piggle-Wiggle. "I love all children. But it makes me sad when I see a child who has something like selfishness, and the father and mother don't do a thing to cure the child."

"But I want to cure Dick," said his mother. "I will do anything to cure him."

Mrs. Piggle-Wiggle said, "The Selfishness Cure is really very easy. But you must do **just** what I tell you. You will have to come down here and get my Selfishness Kit. And I will tell you how to use it."

"Thank you so much, dear Mrs. Piggle-Wiggle," said Mrs. Thompson. "I will leave right now." She put on her coat and ran all the way to Mrs. Piggle-Wiggle's house.

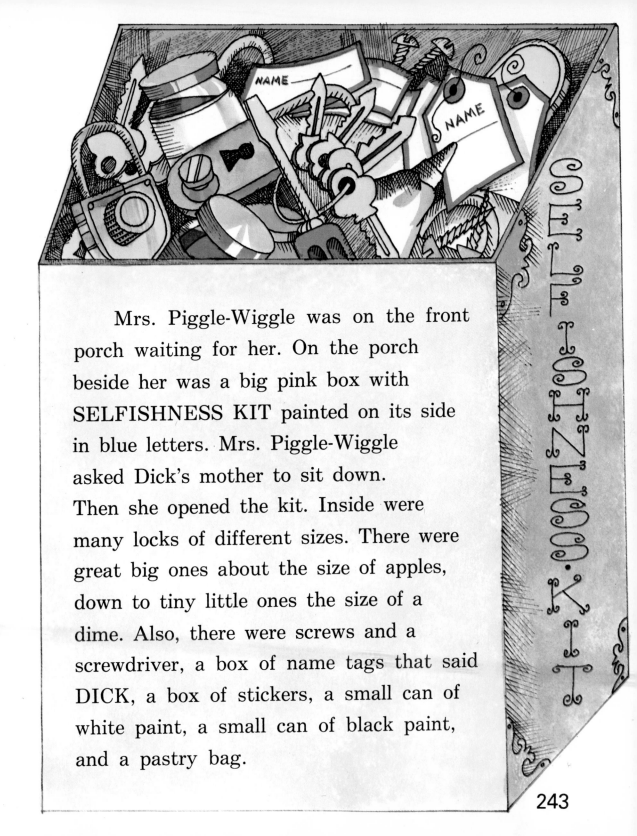

Mrs. Piggle-Wiggle was on the front porch waiting for her. On the porch beside her was a big pink box with SELFISHNESS KIT painted on its side in blue letters. Mrs. Piggle-Wiggle asked Dick's mother to sit down. Then she opened the kit. Inside were many locks of different sizes. There were great big ones about the size of apples, down to tiny little ones the size of a dime. Also, there were screws and a screwdriver, a box of name tags that said DICK, a box of stickers, a small can of white paint, a small can of black paint, and a pastry bag.

243

Mrs. Piggle-Wiggle said,
"Mrs. Thompson, these locks are for all
Dick's things. When you get home, put
these locks on his drawers, his bike,
his bedroom door, his toothbrush and
everything else he owns. Then give him
the keys. This is so that **he** and **he
alone** can touch his things. The name
tags are to be put on all his clothes.
And the stickers are for all his books,
his ruler, his crayons, and his paints.
On each sticker write in big letters
with this black paint DICK'S BOOK—
DON'T TOUCH! or DICK'S CRAYONS
—DON'T TOUCH!

"On every toy you must paint,
in black or white paint, DICK'S BALL—
DON'T TOUCH! or DICK'S BAT—
DON'T TOUCH! Put the name of the
toy first and then DON'T TOUCH!

"The pastry bag is to be filled
with white frosting. It is to be used
to mark Dick's sandwiches, apples,
cookies, and plate.

"That's all there is to it. I'm sure
you won't need the Selfishness Kit
for more than a week."

Mrs. Thompson said, "Are you sure
it will work?"

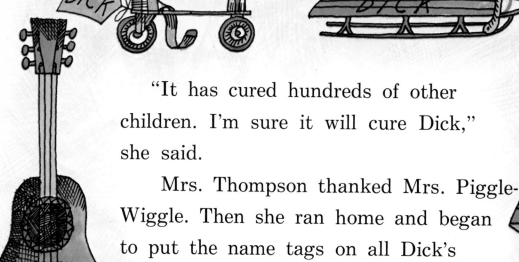

"It has cured hundreds of other children. I'm sure it will cure Dick," she said.

Mrs. Thompson thanked Mrs. Piggle-Wiggle. Then she ran home and began to put the name tags on all Dick's clothes. He asked her what she was doing. When she showed him, he was as happy as could be. "Boy, that will show people who owns my clothes," he said.

Mrs. Thompson did not say anything. She just went right on doing what she was doing. She put name tags on all Dick's clothes, even his socks. Then she opened the kit and took out a tiny lock. She locked Dick's toothbrush to the toothbrush rack. Then she gave the key to Dick. "You should find a ring to hold your keys," she said. "You're going to have a lot of them."

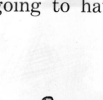

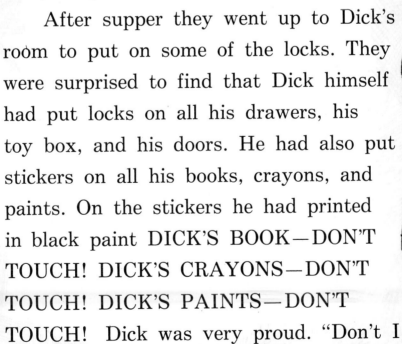

"Boy, that's wonderful!" Dick said, looking at the tiny key. He was thinking, "That's **my** toothbrush, and now no one but **me** can touch it." He was very happy.

When it was time for supper, Mrs. Thompson closed the Selfishness Kit and took it to show Dick's father. She told him about Mrs. Piggle-Wiggle. Mr. Thompson said he was sure everything was going to be all right.

After supper they went up to Dick's room to put on some of the locks. They were surprised to find that Dick himself had put locks on all his drawers, his toy box, and his doors. He had also put stickers on all his books, crayons, and paints. On the stickers he had printed in black paint DICK'S BOOK—DON'T TOUCH! DICK'S CRAYONS—DON'T TOUCH! DICK'S PAINTS—DON'T TOUCH! Dick was very proud. "Don't I print well?" he asked his father.

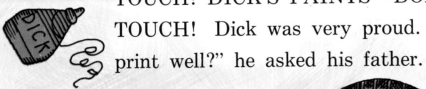

His father said, "You should be able to print well. You've had a lot of practice." And he looked sadly around the room at all the stickers.

He turned to Dick's mother and said, "Maybe we should also wear stickers. DICK'S MOTHER—DON'T TOUCH! DICK'S FATHER—DON'T TOUCH!"

Mrs. Thompson did not laugh.

Then Dick said, "Come on, let's mark all the rest of my things."

And so they worked until nine. They marked Dick's bike, his baseball, his bat, his pitcher's glove, his catcher's glove, his tool box, his lunchbox, and his toy ships. They even painted DICK'S DOG—DON'T TOUCH! on Willie's collar.

When Dick had gone to bed, Mr. Thompson sank down into a chair. "I hope that Mrs. Piggle-Wiggle knows what she's doing," he said. "If this cure doesn't work, our son is going to be the most awful boy in the whole world."

Mrs. Thompson said, "Oh, no, dear, not in the whole world!"

Part Three
The Selfishness Cure

The next morning they could hear Dick working at his locks long before they were up. He was a little late coming down to breakfast because it took time to lock all his drawers and doors. But he was very happy.

While Dick was eating his breakfast, his mother packed his lunch. She marked the sandwiches, the apple, and his cookies. She marked his lunchbox, too.

After breakfast Dick put his lunchbox in his basket. He noticed the big sign on his bike. It said DICK'S BIKE—DON'T TOUCH!

At school the children didn't notice
the sign on his bike. At lunch he opened
his lunchbox and took out the sandwiches.
They were marked DICK'S SAND-
WICHES—DON'T TOUCH! The apple
was marked DICK'S APPLE—DON'T
TOUCH! and the cookies were marked
DICK'S COOKIES—DON'T TOUCH!
Everyone laughed and wanted to see
them. With all the pushing, one of the
sandwiches fell and was jumped on.
Then some of the children took the apple
and threw it in the air. "Throw me
Dick's apple," they yelled. "Oh, look,
Dick's apple fell on the ground." When
at last they gave Dick his apple, it was
brown and soft.

That afternoon Peter Lincoln asked Dick for his ruler. When he saw the sticker that said DICK'S RULER—DON'T TOUCH! he began to laugh. He gave the ruler to Tom Howard, who laughed, too. Tom gave it to the girl in front of him. Mrs. Fisher had to come down to get it. When she saw the sign, she laughed, too. But she gave the ruler back to Dick.

DICK'S RULER-DON'T TOUCH!

After school some of the children decided to play baseball in the lot by Dick's house. Dick brought out his ball and bat, and everyone saw DICK'S BALL—DON'T TOUCH! DICK'S BAT —DON'T TOUCH! "We can't touch anything so let's go home," they said. And they went home.

Dick went up to his room to play. But he found that he had locked the key to his toy box in another box. So he went down and sat on the front porch. He listened to the children playing in Butch Brown's yard.

The next morning at school, no one would play with him. The boys and girls pointed at him, and they laughed and laughed. Mrs. Fisher came to see what the trouble was. She almost laughed herself when she saw the sign someone had put on the back of Dick's coat. It said "THIS IS DICK—DON'T TOUCH!"

At lunchtime the children gathered around to look at his sandwiches. As soon as Dick took them out, the children danced around him and sang, "Dick's sandwich—Don't touch! Dick's apple—Don't touch! Dick's lunchbox— Don't touch!"

After school Dick went right home,
but he had lost the key to his room.
So he went down to play with his
tool box. But every time he saw the big
white sign DICK'S TOOL BOX—DON'T
TOUCH! he thought of school and his
lunchbox. He thought of how the children
laughed at him. He felt just awful. At
supper his father brought him his plate
marked DICK'S DINNER—DON'T
TOUCH! Dick looked at it and said,
"Aw, why do you have to mark my plate?
I don't care which one I get."

Mrs. Thompson smiled at Mr. Thompson and said, "All right, Dick, we won't mark your plate if you will share your cake with Willie."

Dick thought for a while and then divided his cake into two parts. He gave one to Willie, who ate it down and looked happy.

After dinner Dick told his father he had lost the keys to his room. And so his father took off the locks on his doors and on the toy box. Dick said, "Don't put them back, Dad. I don't care who goes into my room or gets into my things."

MINE?

The next morning Dick got up
at six o'clock. He scraped DICK'S
LUNCHBOX—DON'T TOUCH! from his
lunchbox. He took the sign off his bike.
Then he went in to his mother. "Mom,"
he said, "please don't mark my sandwiches.
Please don't mark any of my things, Mom."

Mrs. Thompson said, "All right, Dick.
I only did it to help you."

Dick said, "I don't care who gets
my lunch. Just don't mark it."

At lunch all the children gathered
around. But his sandwiches, and his
apple, and his lunchbox were not marked.
So they ran out to see his bike. There
was no sign on it, so they sat down and
ate their lunches.

Right after school Dick ran home and scraped the marking off his bat and ball. Then he scraped the DICK'S GLOVE—DON'T TOUCH! off his glove, and walked up to where the children were playing ball. He threw the ball, bat, and glove down beside the catcher. "Do you want to use these?" he asked. "I don't care," he said, and he went back to his own house.

In a little while Kim James rang
the doorbell. She asked Mrs. Thompson
if Dick could come out and play.
Mrs. Thompson said, "He'd love to, Kim.
But first he must return something
to Mrs. Piggle-Wiggle."

Kim said, "Tell him to come over
to the lot when he gets back. And here
are some keys he lost."

SELFISHNESS KIT

Mrs. Thompson said, "Thank you for the keys, dear. But thank goodness they are Mrs. Piggle-Wiggles's, not Dick's."

She took the keys up to Dick who was in his room. He was very busy packing Mrs. Piggle-Wiggle's Selfishness Kit.

Poetry
of the
Papago Indian Tribe

Come all! Stand up!
Just over there the dawn is coming.
Now I hear
Soft laughter.

At the edge of the world
It is growing light.
The trees stand shining.
I like it.
It is growing light.

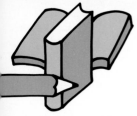

Another Way to Say It

Look at these pictures. Read the words below the pictures.

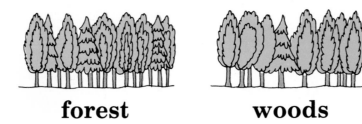

forest   **woods**

The words <u>forest</u> and <u>woods</u> have nearly the same meaning. Read these words.

day   **night**

The words <u>day</u> and <u>night</u> do *not* have the same meaning at all.

A. Write each set of words on your paper. Write <u>yes</u> after a set if the words have nearly the same meaning. Write <u>no</u> if they do not.

1. collected   gathered   _yes_
2. high   low   _____
3. unhappy   sad   _____
4. during   while   _____
5. push   pull   _____
6. imagine   pretend   _____
7. before   after   _____

B. Read each group of words below. Look at the first word. Choose another word that has nearly the same meaning. Write that word on your paper.

1. <u>rock</u>   stone   throw   ground
   1. stone
2. <u>fast</u>   slow   quick   stop
3. <u>afraid</u>   boy   stared   scared
4. <u>all</u>   none   every   some
5. <u>evening</u>   day   night   morning
6. <u>awful</u>   nice   good   bad
7. <u>stop</u>   begin   end   start

A SECOND LOOK

Each person sees the world in a
different way from anyone else.
The way you see the world helps
you decide how to act.

Thinking About "A Second Look"

1. Why will the Thomas family still
   keep thinking about the mirror
   even though the mirror is broken?
2. Why do you think Ginny and
   Miyoko will go on being friends?
3. Why won't the ghosts ever bother
   Ved again?
4. Why won't Dick Thompson start
   being selfish again?
5. What kinds of things do others do
   that help you decide how to act?

Glossary

265

A

a · ble   Having the power or skill to do something. A deer is <u>able</u> to run very fast.

a · cross   On the other side of. They visited the house <u>across</u> the lake.

al · read · y   Before now. We have <u>already</u> eaten.

ap · ple   A round fruit we eat that grows on trees. The <u>apple</u> fell from the tree.

at · tic   The part of a house just below the roof. Our <u>attic</u> is filled with old books.

B

back · ache   A hurt in the back. I had a <u>backache</u> after I fell off my bike.

bath · ing   Washing oneself or another in water. She is <u>bathing</u> the dog in the lake.

beau · ti · ful   Pleasant to look at or hear. A <u>beautiful</u> red flower grew in the woods.

be · side   Next to. Harry sat <u>beside</u> Anita.

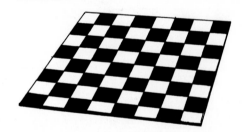

board   A flat piece of wood, cardboard, or something else used in many games. Get the <u>board</u> and we'll play a game of checkers.

born   Brought into life. Those tiny kittens were <u>born</u> last week.

both   The two. <u>Both</u> letters are mine.

266

both · er   To trouble or annoy. Loud music may <u>bother</u> some people.

bought   Got after paying. We <u>bought</u> cauliflower at the store.

bridge   Something built across a river or road so that people can get from one side to the other. We drove the car across the <u>bridge</u>.

brought   Caused someone or something to come with you. He <u>brought</u> his lunch when he came to school.

built   Made. They <u>built</u> a doghouse in the backyard.

but · ter · fly   An insect with brightly colored wings. The <u>butterfly</u> flew to the flower.

C

cac · tus   A kind of plant that grows in a dry place. The <u>cactus</u> has small yellow flowers.

can · dle · light   The light from a burning candle. We ate dinner by <u>candlelight</u>.

cap · tain   A leader. They picked her to be <u>captain</u> of their team.

cat · tle   Animals, such as cows, used for meat and milk. The rancher feeds the <u>cattle</u> every day.

caught   Held or trapped. My hair was <u>caught</u> on a branch.

chalk   Something to draw or write with. Ben drew on the board with green <u>chalk</u>.

change   To make or become different. Leaves <u>change</u> color in the fall.

check • ers A game for two people played on a board. Let's play one game of <u>checkers</u> before bedtime.

cheer To make or become happy. The sunlight in the window helped to <u>cheer</u> up the sick boy.

clear Without clouds, bright. The day was warm and <u>clear</u>.

clothes Things worn to cover the body. I packed some <u>clothes</u> for my trip.

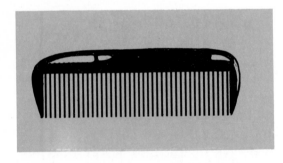

comb A tool used to fix hair. Winifred used a <u>comb</u> to put her hair in place.

con • grat • u • la • tions Words said to tell a person that he or she has done well. She gave her <u>congratulations</u> to the winner of the race.

cor • ner The place where two walls come together. She put a lamp in the <u>corner</u> of the room.

course A way of acting. **of course.** certainly, naturally. Of <u>course</u> I will go with you.

coy • o • te An animal that is part of the dog family. The <u>coyote</u> was hunting for food in the field.

co • zy Warm and safe. The kitten sleeps in a <u>cozy</u> spot by the fire.

cured Made well again. I <u>cured</u> my cold by resting in bed.

D

daugh • ter A girl child. Their <u>daughter</u> is one year older than their son.

dear A word of surprise or trouble. "Oh <u>dear</u>!" she cried when she fell.

dif · fer · ence   A way of being unlike or different. Do you see a difference between the two puppies?

din · ing   Eating dinner. We will be dining at home tomorrow.

dis · gust   To make feel sick. It disgusts her to see garbage in the street.

di · vide   To separate into parts, pieces, or groups. We will divide the work among us.

drew   Made a picture. He drew pictures of castles and clouds.

dur · ing   Throughout the course of. We will be away during July.

E

earth · quake   A shaking of the ground. The earthquake frightened many people.

eas · y   Not hard. It is easy to make friends.

ei · ther   One or the other. There were no houses on either side of the country road.

else   Other or different. Someone else will drive the bus.

e · nough   The amount needed. There is just enough room for all of us.

F

fa · ble   A story that teaches a lesson. Do you know the fable about the ant and the grasshopper?

fan   A person who likes something very much. She is a baseball fan and never misses a game.

fence   Something built around a field or a house. The farmer built a fence around the cornfield.

field   A place where games are played. The players left the field after the game.

fi · nal · ly   At the end, at last. We <u>finally</u> got to play baseball after it stopped raining.

fin · ger   One of the five parts at the end of the hand. He wears a ring on his <u>finger</u>.

fish · er · men   People who catch fish for a living. The <u>fishermen</u> went out in their boats.

floor   The part of a room people walk or stand on. He did not walk on the wet <u>floor</u>.

folk · tale   A story that has been handed down among the common people. Max read the African <u>folktale</u> to the class.

fol · lowed   Went or came after. The baby duck <u>followed</u> its mother.

fool · ish   Silly. The dog looked <u>foolish</u> wearing a hat.

fourth   Next after third. She stood <u>fourth</u> in line for her turn in the game.

frost · ing   A sweet covering for cakes or cookies. He put pink <u>frosting</u> on the cake.

G

gar · den   A piece of ground where plants are grown. In spring, the plants in the <u>garden</u> are just little green shoots.

ga · thered   Came or brought together. Betsy <u>gathered</u> the apples and put them into a bag.

ghost   The supposed spirit of a dead person. Jane dressed as a <u>ghost</u> for Halloween.

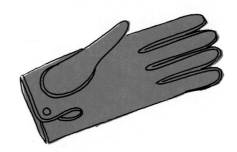

glove   A covering for the hand. His <u>glove</u> was wet because he had been throwing snowballs.

great-grand · fa · ther   The father of someone's grandfather or grandmother. My <u>great-grandfather</u> lives with us.

H

ham   The meat from the back leg of a pig. We baked a <u>ham</u> for dinner.

hand·ker·chief   A piece of cloth used to wipe the nose or face. He used a <u>handkerchief</u> when he had a cold.

hap·pened   Took place by chance. She <u>happened</u> to see the letter under the door.

haunt·ed   Lived in. People say that ghosts <u>haunted</u> the old house.

he'd   A short way to say "he would." Sam said <u>he'd</u> like to come to the party.

high·er   Taller. A mountain is <u>higher</u> than a hill.

hour   60 minutes. I practice the piano for one <u>hour</u> every day.

I

im·pos·si·ble   Not able to happen or be done. It is <u>impossible</u> to see in the dark.

J

jol·ly   Full of fun. The clown in the circus is very <u>jolly</u>.

jun·gle   A hot, wet forest. Monkeys live in the trees in the <u>jungle</u>.

K

kept   Went on or continued. I <u>kept</u> on reading until I came to the end of the book.

key   Something used to open a lock. I lost my <u>key</u>, so I couldn't open the door.

271

kind · ly　In a nice way. The girl kindly climbed the tree to get the cat.

kit　A collection of parts or things to put together. Kim bought a toy airplane kit.

knee-high　As high as the knee. The water where we were fishing was only knee-high.

L

la · zy　Not wanting to work. The lazy girl would not clean up her room.

league　A number of people or groups joined together for the same purpose. Five teams belong to our league.

left　Went from. She left the park to go to the store.

leg　The part of the body used to stand or to walk on. Her leg hurt after she walked all day.

lock　Something to put on a door, window, box, or trunk to keep it closed. I put a lock on the trunk so no one could open it.

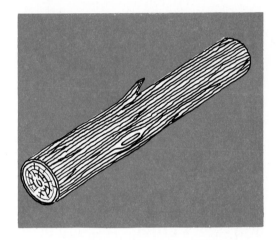

log　A piece of a tree trunk or branch. I put another log on the fire.

M

Maj · es · ty　A word used to talk to or about a king or queen. His Majesty, the king, lived in the royal palace.

mark · ings　Spots or lines. I can tell which kitten is mine by its markings.

272

min · ute   A short time. It only takes a <u>minute</u> to walk next door.

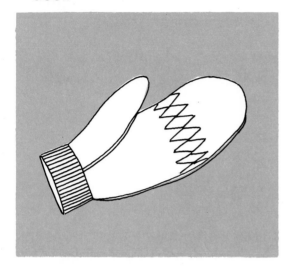

mit · ten   A covering for the hand to keep it warm. He lost one <u>mitten</u>, so one hand got cold.

mo · hair   The hair of a goat or cloth made from it. She wore a cap made of <u>mohair</u>.

Mon · day   The second day of the week. School begins next <u>Monday</u>.

moss   A small green plant that grows on rocks, trees, and the ground. <u>Moss</u> often grows on the north side of trees.

N

nap   A short sleep. He took a <u>nap</u> before he went to the party.

ner · vous   Jumpy, scared, upset. John was <u>nervous</u> before he played the piano for the class.

no · bod · y   Not one person. <u>Nobody</u> guessed the surprise.

none   Nothing, not one. My sister ate the last cookie so <u>none</u> were left for me.

no · ticed   Saw or looked at. I <u>noticed</u> the new house on the street.

O

o · cean   The sea. We swam in the <u>ocean</u> when we visited Hawaii.

of · ten   Many times. I <u>often</u> go to the park after school.

o · kay   A form of the word "O.K.," meaning "all right." <u>Okay</u>, I'll feed the cat.

owl   A kind of bird that hunts for food at night. The <u>owl</u> flew low over the ground looking for a mouse to eat.

P

pad · dle   To move the hands or feet in water. My sister likes to <u>paddle</u> in the pool.

page   A boy or girl who runs errands for someone else. She worked as a <u>page</u> in the hotel.

pal · ace   A royal castle. The king and queen live in the <u>palace</u>.

pas · try   Something sweet to eat. The children ate the fresh apple <u>pastry</u> their mother had baked.

pep · per · mint   A flavor made from a plant, used to give a special taste. The <u>peppermint</u> tasted cool and sweet.

per · son   A man, woman, or child. Every <u>person</u> is in some way special.

piece   A single thing that is part of a whole or a group. I ate a <u>piece</u> of the cake my mother made.

pleas · ant · est   Most pleasant. A walk in the woods is the <u>pleasantest</u> thing!

poor   Having little money. They were too <u>poor</u> to buy new shoes.

pos · sum   A small animal with brown fur and a long tail. When a <u>possum</u> is afraid, it lies very quiet and still.

prac · ticed   Did some action over and over. The class <u>practiced</u> the play for three weeks.

pre · sent   To give. Our class will <u>present</u> a play for the rest of the school.

274

prom · ise   To give one's word. I <u>promise</u> not to tell anyone about the surprise birthday party.

pu · ma   A mountain lion that is part of the cat family. The <u>puma</u> lives in the jungle in South America.

pup · pet   A small doll that looks like a person or an animal and has parts that can be moved. Sandy has a <u>puppet</u> that looks like a clown.

puz · zled   Confused. A <u>puzzled</u> look came over her face.

quite   Really or very much. She was <u>quite</u> full after she ate all those cookies.

quit · ter   A person who gives up or stops doing something. He tried again because he was not a <u>quitter</u>.

race   To run to see who runs fastest. They had to <u>race</u> from one end of the field to the other.

ranch   A big farm where people keep horses and cattle. There are many horses on a big <u>ranch</u>.

rath · er   More willingly. I would <u>rather</u> read than watch TV.

re · flec · tion   A picture given back by something flat and shiny. I saw my <u>reflection</u> in the mirror.

re • mark • a • ble   Unusual, not ordinary. It is <u>remarkable</u> how tall you've grown in the last year.

rice   The grains from plants that grow in warm places. I like <u>rice</u> better than potatoes.

roared   Made a loud, deep sound or cry. The car <u>roared</u> down the street.

roll • ing   Moving by turning over and over. The hoops are <u>rolling</u> down the hill.

roof   The outer covering of the top of a house. When it rains, the <u>roof</u> leaks.

roy • al   Of or having to do with a king or a queen. The princess lives in the <u>royal</u> palace with her mother, the queen.

rul • er   A strip of wood, metal, or plastic marked into units. The teacher used a <u>ruler</u> to measure the desk.

S

sad • ly   In an unhappy way. He watched <u>sadly</u> as his friends drove away.

save   To make safe or keep from being hurt. The woman ran to <u>save</u> the girl.

screw • driv • er   A tool for turning screws. She used a <u>screwdriver</u> to fix the lock on the door.

sea • shore   The land near the sea. I found those shells at the <u>seashore</u>.

se • cret   Hidden. My <u>secret</u> playhouse is in the woods where no one can find it.

self-por·trait   A picture one paints or draws of himself or herself. When Fred painted his self-portrait, he used a mirror to see himself.

share   To use with another or others. She wanted to share her books with her friends.

shav·ing   Removing hair with a razor. My father is shaving off his beard.

sighed   Made a long, deep breathing sound because of being tired or sad. She sat down and sighed when she finished her work.

sol·dier   A person who belongs to the army. The soldier marched in the parade.

spar·kle   To look bright. The snow sparkles in the sunlight.

squeeze   To press hard. If you squeeze the orange, you will get juice.

stom·ach   The part of the body where food goes after it is eaten. My stomach hurts when I eat too much.

straight   Without a bend. He drew a straight line on his paper.

suit   A set of clothes. My father put on a suit for the meeting.

sup·per   A meal eaten in the evening. He ate supper just before he went to bed.

T

tai·lor   A person who makes clothes. The tailor made a suit for my father.

taught   Helped to learn. My brother taught me to read.

these   The people or things nearby or just talked about. These are my friends.

tip·toe   To move or walk quietly on one's toes. If I tiptoe, no one will hear me leave the room.

to·mor·row   The day after today. We are going to leave for vacation tomorrow.

to·night   The night of this day. I am going to my grandmother's for dinner tonight.

touch   To put a hand or other part of the body on or against something. Do not <u>touch</u> things in the museum.

trou · ble   A difficult or dangerous situation. Nan saw that the boat was in <u>trouble</u>.

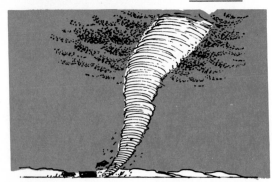

twist · er   A wind storm. The <u>twister</u> lifted the house from the ground.

U

un · der · stand   To get the meaning of. They <u>understand</u> the story she is reading.

V

va · ca · tion   A time of rest. During summer <u>vacation</u>, I went to a ranch.

verse   Part of a poem or a song. I remembered every <u>verse</u> of the poem.

wear   To dress in, to put on. He wanted to <u>wear</u> his new hat, but it was raining.

which   What one. <u>Which</u> of the crayons would you like to use?

whole   All, not just part. We ate the <u>whole</u> watermelon.

wil · low   A tree with long branches that bend. The branches of the <u>willow</u> tree were so long they touched the ground.

won · der · ful   Very good or amazing. She taught her cat a <u>wonderful</u> trick.

wor · ry   To feel or make to feel uneasy or troubled. I told him not to <u>worry</u> about the weather.

wrote   Put words on paper or on something else. I <u>wrote</u> a letter to my friend who moved last year.